G000055414

HEADWAY VIDEO

ACTIVITY BOOK PRE-INTERMEDIATE

Tim Falla

Series editors John & Liz Soars

نام كتاب: HEADWAY VIDEO · PRE-INTERMEDIATE

ناشر: پیک زبان

لیتوگرافی: درخشان ـ م ـ آ شوری ۶۷۰۹۷۲۸

چاپ: چاپ و نشر معرفت

نوبت چاپ: دوم ۱۳۷۹

تیراژ: ۱۰۰۰۰

قیمت: ۲۵۰۰۰ ریال

آدرس: تهران ـ شهرآرا ـ بلوار شرقی ـ بلوک ۲۲ ـ پلاک ۲۰

تلفن: ۸۲۶۶۸۶۵ تلفن همراه ۹۱۱۲۳۴۶۸۵۱

مرکز پخش : تهران ـ کارگر شمالی ـ مرکز خود اشتغالی شماره ۱

موسسه فرهنگی و انتشاراتی زبان افشان

تلفن: ۶۵۵۲۶۴

Oxford University Press

Oxford University Press
Great Clarendon Street, Oxford OX2 6DP

Oxford New York
Athens Auckland Bangkok Bogota Bombay
Buenos Aires Calcutta Cape Town Dar es Salaam
Delhi Florence Hong Kong Istanbul Karachi
Kuala Lumpur Madras Madrid Melbourne
Mexico City Nairobi Paris Singapore
Taipei Tokyo Toronto Warsaw

and associated companies in
Berlin Ibadan

Oxford and Oxford English are
trade marks of Oxford University Press

First published 1994
Fifth impression 1998

ISBN 0 19 458823 8   (Activity Book)
ISBN 0 19 458824 6   (Video Guide)

ISBN 0 19 458825 4   (VHS PAL Video Cassette 1)
ISBN 0 19 458827 0   (VHS SECAM Video Cassette 1)
ISBN 0 19 458829 7   (VHS NTSC Video Cassette 1)
ISBN 0 19 458831 9   (VHS PAL Video Cassette 2)
ISBN 0 19 458833 5   (VHS SECAM Video Cassette 2)
ISBN 0 19 458835 1   (VHS NTSC Video Cassette 2)

ISBN 0 19 458826 2   (BETAMAX PAL Video Cassette 1)
ISBN 0 19 458828 9   (BETAMAX SECAM Video Cassette 1)
ISBN 0 19 458830 0   (BETAMAX NTSC Video Cassette 1)
ISBN 0 19 458832 7   (BETAMAX PAL Video Cassette 2)
ISBN 0 19 458834 3   (BETAMAX SECAM Video Cassette 2)
ISBN 0 19 458836 X   (BETAMAX NTSC Video Cassette 2)

© Oxford University Press, 1994

No unauthorized photocopying

All rights reserved. No part of this publication may be
reproduced, stored in a retrieval system, or transmitted,
in any form or by any means, electronic, mechanical,
photocopying, recording, or otherwise, without the prior
written permission of Oxford University Press.

This book is sold subject to the condition that it shall not,
by way of trade or otherwise, be lent, resold, hired out or
otherwise circulated without the publisher's prior consent
in any form of binding or cover other than that in which it
is published and without a similar condition including this
condition being imposed on the subsequent purchaser.

Printed in Hong Kong

ACKNOWLEDGEMENTS

*The publishers would like to thank the following for permission to
reproduce photographs:*
Allsport UK Ltd
The British Film Institute/Hammer Films
The British Motor Industry Heritage Trust
BBC Photograph Library and Archive
BBC World Service
Barnaby's Picture Library/A Bruce
Camera Press/Norman Parkinson
Colorific!/Peter Turnley
Mary Evans Picture Library/Wordsworth Editions Ltd.
Falla Classics, MG Restoration and Sales, Bournemouth
Ferrari UK
Ford Motor Company Ltd
Fotomas Index
The National Motor Museum, Beaulieu
Michael Pointer Collection
Rolls Royce Motor Cars
Topham Picturepoint
Mrs Margaret Tombs
Volkswagen
Welsh Folk Museum

*Every effort has been made to trace the owners of copyright
material used in this book, but we should be pleased to hear from
any copyright holder whom we have been unable to contact.*

Stills photography by Rob Judges
Studio photography by Mark Mason Studios

Illustrations by:
Mike Allport
Martin Cottam
Roger Fereday
Phil Hall
Rob Hancock
Michael Hill
Ian Moores
Julie O'Sullivan
Tim Slade
Martin Ursell

AUTHOR'S ACKNOWLEDGEMENT

*I should like to thank Liz and John Soars for their support,
encouragement, and advice.*

Contents

Syllabus		4
Situation	**1 ▷ THE STATION**	5
Report	**2 ▷ SHERLOCK HOLMES**	10
Situation	**3 ▷ CAR HIRE**	15
Report	**4 ▷ PURPLE VIOLIN**	20
Situation	**5 ▷ THE HOTEL**	26
Report	**6 ▷ WALES**	31
Report	**7 ▷ BBC WORLD SERVICE**	39
Situation	**8 ▷ LOST PROPERTY**	46
Report	**9 ▷ THE MINI**	51
Situation	**10 ▷ INTRODUCTIONS**	57
Report	**11 ▷ THE VILLAGE**	62
Situation	**12 ▷ FAREWELL**	68
Transcript		73

Main points of the syllabus

1 ▷ THE STATION

Greetings
Train information and timetables

2 ▷ SHERLOCK HOLMES

Present simple
Focus on Language: past simple

3 ▷ CAR HIRE

Hiring a car
Focus on Language: polite requests

4 ▷ PURPLE VIOLIN

Present simple
Past simple
going to
Focus on Language: verb patterns

5 ▷ THE HOTEL

Making and responding to complaints
Ordering from room service

6 ▷ WALES

Present simple
Past simple
Present perfect
should
Focus on Language: *have to*

7 ▷ BBC WORLD SERVICE

Present simple
Past simple
Past continuous
Focus on Language: *used to*

8 ▷ LOST PROPERTY

Reporting lost property to the police

9 ▷ THE MINI

Past simple
Present perfect
Superlatives
Focus on Language: the passive

10 ▷ INTRODUCTIONS

Introducing people
Meeting people for the first time

11 ▷ THE VILLAGE

Present perfect
used to
Passive
Focus on Language: tense review
                     second conditional

12 ▷ FAREWELL

Saying goodbye

1 ▷ THE STATION

Before you watch

1 Look at the photos. What do you think happens? What are the people saying to each other?

2 Fill in the gaps with words from the box.

> article   platform   apologize
> magazine   approximately   hire

a) *Vogue* is a famous fashion _ _ _ _ _ .

b) I read an interesting _ _ _ _ _ on French wine in the newspaper yesterday.

c) 'How are you getting to Oxford? By train?'
  'No, we're going to _ _ _ _ _ a car.'

d) 'The London train comes in at _ _ _ _ _ 2.'

e) 'We would like to _ _ _ _ _ to passengers waiting for the Bristol service. This train is running _ _ _ _ _ five minutes late.'

While you watch

▷ **Watch the whole video and check your ideas for exercise 1.**

SECTION ONE

(*Paola's letter*)

Read Paola's letter and fill in the gaps.

Map showing London, Bath, Padstow, and CORNWALL.

Dear David,

How are you? I'm [ ] it's so long since I wrote to you, but I've been really busy looking for [ ] And at last I've got a job! A magazine called 'In Viaggio' is sending me to Britain in [ ] to take photos for an article on Cornwall. Can I [ ] you in Bath on my way there? I'm arriving on 22nd January. I can't stay very long but it would be [ ] to see you again.

Please write soon and let me [ ] if you'll be in Bath at that time. Sorry this is such a [ ] letter – I'll give you my news when I see you!

[ ]

Paola

▷ **Watch and check.**

SECTION TWO

(to the arrival of Paola's train)

1 ▷ **Listen to the station announcements and fill in the missing information on the screen below.**

2 **What time did Paola's train leave London?**

ⓘ Information

FROM	TO	PLATFORM	TIME	MINUTES LATE
BRISTOL TEMPLE MEADS	LONDON PADDINGTON	2	13.	—
PORTSMOUTH	CARDIFF CENTRAL	1		
LONDON PADDINGTON	BRISTOL TEMPLE MEADS	1		—

SECTION THREE

(to the end)

1 Fill in the gaps with adjectives.

David: It's _ _ _ _ _ to see you. You're looking _ _ _ _ _ .

Paola: So are you! Oh, roses! How _ _ _ _ _ ! Thank you.

David: Here, let me take your case. What have you got in here?

Paola: It's not that _ _ _ _ _ , David!

David: How was the journey?

Paola: Not _ _ _ _ _ . I'm a bit _ _ _ _ _ , though.

David: What time did you leave Rome?

Paola: Oh, eight o'clock. But I got up at half past five.

David: Are you _ _ _ _ _ ?

Paola: No. I had a sandwich on the train.

2 Who says these things? Write D for David or P for Paola. Then put the sentences in the correct order to make a conversation.

☐ ☐ My parents live down there. I was thinking of going to see them at the weekend. Perhaps we could meet up – I could even introduce you to them.

☐ ☐ I'm going to hire a car. The magazine is paying. But thanks anyway.

☐ 1 When are you going to Cornwall?

☐ ☐ Oh, don't worry. I won't get in your way.

☐ ☐ No, it's OK. Look, if you've got time, we can meet up. If not, well, never mind. I could drive you down to Cornwall if you like.

☐ ☐ Tomorrow.

☐ ☐ Oh, I didn't mean that. Just …

☐ ☐ Yes, that would be nice, but I've got a lot of work to do.

▶ *Watch and check.*

Review

Are these sentences true ☑ **or false** ☒ **? Correct the false sentences.**

		TRUE	FALSE
1	In her letter Paola says she is coming to Britain in July.	☐	☐
2	Paola's train will arrive at 1.45.	☐	☐
3	David gives Paola yellow roses.	☐	☐
4	David thinks that Paola's case is very heavy.	☐	☐
5	Paola left Rome at 5.30.	☐	☐
6	Paola ate on the train.	☐	☐
7	David's parents live in Bath.	☐	☐
8	Paola is going to Cornwall by train.	☐	☐

After you watch

Summary

ASKING FOR INFORMATION ABOUT TRAINS

Can you tell me which platform the 1.45 from London comes in at?

Is the train running on time?

MEETING SOMEBODY

It's great to see you.

You're looking well! (So are you.)

Let me take your case.

How was the journey? (Not bad …)

What time did you leave Rome?

I had a sandwich on the train.

ACTIVITY ONE

Role-play: ASKING FOR INFORMATION ABOUT TRAINS

Student A:

You are at Bath station. Your friend is arriving on the 15.32 from London. Ask the porter which platform the train will come in at. Then ask if it's running on time.

Student B:

It's three o'clock. You want to catch the next train to London. Find out the time and platform from the porter.

Student C:

You are a porter at Bath station. Students A and B want information about trains. Use the information below to answer their questions.

Ask and answer questions about different trains. Then change roles.

ACTIVITY TWO

Role-play: MEETING SOMEBODY

In pairs practise the conversation in SECTION THREE, exercise 1, on page 8.

Student A:

A friend from Britain is coming to visit you. You are going to meet them at the station or airport. When they arrive, offer to take their cases, ask about the journey, etc. (You can give them some flowers, too, if you like!)

Student B:

You have come from Britain to stay with your friend, Student A. When you arrive, greet them and tell them about your journey.

ACTIVITY THREE

You are going to visit a friend in Britain. Write a letter to them saying when and where you are arriving.

Information: arrivals and departures

From	To	Platform	Arrives	Departs	Minutes late
Bath	London Paddington	1	15.23	15.25	
Southampton	Bath	1	15.28	15.30	8
London Paddington	Bath	2	15.32	15.34	4
Bristol Temple Meads	Bath	1	15.45	15.47	
Weymouth	Bath	1	15.49	15.51	7
Bath	Cardiff	2	15.55	15.57	
Bath	Bristol Temple Meads	2	15.57	15.59	25
London Paddington	Bath	2	16.02	16.04	
Bath	Southampton	2	16.07	16.09	12

2 ▷ SHERLOCK HOLMES

SECTION THREE

(*to* **Amanda:** ... 'more a machine than a man.')

WAS HOLMES A HAPPY MAN?

» FOCUS ON LANGUAGE «
past simple

Fill in the gaps using verbs from the box. Put them in the past simple (positive or negative).

> fall in love   understand   spend
> describe   say   marry   share   take (×2)
> be (×3)   become   think

Amanda: Although he _ _ _ _ _ very clever and successful, Holmes _ _ _ _ _ a rather sad person. He _ _ _ _ _ everyday life _ _ _ _ _ boring and depressing. When he was feeling miserable or bored, h _ _ _ _ _ all day in bed. And sometimes he _ _ _ _ _ drugs.

Holmes: Drugs?

Amanda: Yes. He _ _ _ _ _ cocaine – before it _ _ _ _ _ illegal, of course. He _ _ _ _ _ his flat with his only friend, Dr Watson. Holmes never _ _ _ _ _ , and he never _ _ _ _ _ . He _ _ _ _ _ that he _ _ _ _ _ women. Dr Watson _ _ _ _ _ him as 'a brain without a heart', 'more a machine than a man'.

> ▶ **Watch and check.**

SECTION FOUR

(*to the end*)

WHO WROTE THE HOLMES STORIES?

> ▶ **Watch and then answer these questions.**

1 What was Arthur Conan Doyles' job?

_ _

2 In the story called *The Final Problem*, how did Holmes die?

_ _ _ _ _ _ _ _ _ _ _ _ _ _ _

_ _ _ _ _ _ _ _ _ _ _ _ _ _ _

_ _ _ _ _ _ _ _ _ _ _ _ _ _ _

Holmes and Moriarty at the Reichenbach Falls

3 What did Conan Doyle think of his Sherlock Holmes stories?

_ _

_ _

4 Why did he decide to kill off Holmes?

_ _

5 Why did he have to bring Holmes back to life?

_ _

Review

Read the summary and fill in the gaps using the adjectives in the box.

> intelligent   illegal   upset
> depressing   everyday   athletic
> famous   serious   superb
> sad   bored

Sherlock Holmes is the most _ _ _ _ _ detective in the world. He lived at 221b Baker Street with his only friend, Dr Watson. Holmes was very _ _ _ _ _ , and he had many abilities. He was strong and _ _ _ _ _ , and he was a _ _ _ _ _ violinist.

But there was another side to his character: he was a rather _ _ _ _ _ person. He thought that _ _ _ _ _ life was _ _ _ _ _ . When he was feeling _ _ _ _ _ , he sometimes took drugs – before they became _ _ _ _ _ , of course! He never fell in love, and he never married. His friend, Watson, described him as 'a brain without a heart'.

The author of the Holmes stories, Arthur Conan Doyle, didn't think his Sherlock Holmes stories were very _ _ _ _ _ . But his readers were very _ _ _ _ _ when he killed Holmes off, so he had to carry on writing detective stories for the rest of his life.

After you watch

ACTIVITY ONE

Reading: A SCANDAL IN BOHEMIA

1 Read the story. Write five questions.

EXAMPLE
Did Holmes ever fall in love?

FOR SHERLOCK HOLMES, there was only one woman in the world. He did not love her, because he never loved women. But after their meeting he never forgot her. Her name was Irene Adler. One night in March I visited my old friend at his home in Baker Street. I was married by now, so I did not often see him.

'Come in, Watson,' he said. 'Sit down. I'm happy to see you, because I've got something to show you. What do you think of this? It arrived in the last post.' It was a letter with no date, name, or address. It said:

'Tonight someone will visit you, to talk about some very secret business. You have helped other important people, and you can, we hope, help us. Be in your room at 7.45 p.m.'

'The paper – what do you think about the paper?' asked Holmes.

I tried to think like Holmes. 'It's expensive, so this person is rich. It's strange paper.'

'Yes, it's not English. If you look at it in the light, you can see that it was made in Bohemia. And a German, I think, wrote the letter. Ah, here comes our man now.' We could hear the horses in the street.

'Shall I leave, Holmes?' I said.

'No, no, I need your help. This will be interesting,' my friend answered. There was a knock at the door.

'Come in!' called Holmes.

A tall, strong man came into the room. He was wearing expensive clothes and a mask over his face.

'You can call me Count von Kramm. I come from Bohemia,' he said. 'My business is most important. Before I tell you about it, do you agree to keep it a secret?'

'I do,' we said together.

'A very important person, who belongs to a royal family, has sent me to ask for your help,' he went on. 'I wear a mask because nobody must know who that person is. I must explain how important this business is. If you cannot help, there will be difficulty and trouble for one of the most important families in Europe – and perhaps a very big scandal. I am talking about the famous House of Ormstein, Kings of Bohemia.'

'I know, Your Majesty,' said Holmes. He quietly smoked his cigarette.

The man jumped from his chair. 'What!' he cried. 'How do you know who I am?' Then he pulled the mask from his face and threw it on the ground. 'You are right. Why do I hide it? I am the King. I am Wilhelm von Ormstein, King of Bohemia. I came to see you myself because I could not ask another person to tell my story. It must be a secret. You understand?'

'Very well. Go on,' said Holmes. He closed his eyes and listened.

'Five years ago I met a woman called Irene Adler. We ...'

2 Work in pairs. Close your books and ask and answer the questions.

If you would like to read the rest of the story, it can be found in *Sherlock Holmes Short Stories*, Arthur Conan Doyle, Oxford Bookworms, level 2.

ACTIVITY TWO

1 Write a letter to Sherlock Holmes.

2 Swap letters with a partner. Imagine you are Holmes and write a reply.

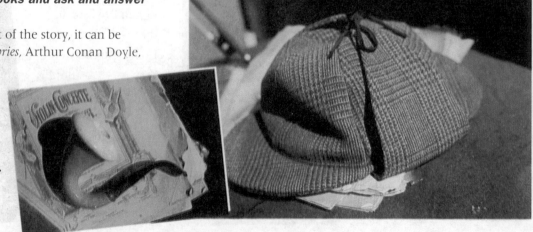

3 ▶ CAR HIRE

Before you watch

Have you or your family ever hired a car? Why?
How much did it cost?
What information did you give?
Where did you go?

*Match words from column A with
words from column B.*

A	B
driving	fine
parking	tank
unlimited	licence
credit	card
petrol	mileage
speeding	ticket

While you watch

Who do you think says these things? Write D for David,
P for Paola, or C for clerk.

2 ▶ **Listen to Paola's conversation with the clerk**
and complete the details on the form.

☐ Can you manage on your own?
☐ Yes, no problem.

☐ Can I help you?
☐ Yes, I'd like to hire a car.

☐ How would you like to pay?
☐ By credit card. Visa.

☐ Could I see your driving licence, please?

☐ Do you know the telephone number?
☐ No, I'm afraid I don't.

☐ If you could just sign here.

☐ We drive on the left, don't forget.
☐ Very funny!

▶ **Watch the whole video and check your answers.**

SECTION ONE

(*to* **Clerk:** Thank you. *After Paola has handed over credit card.*)

1 Are these sentences true or false?

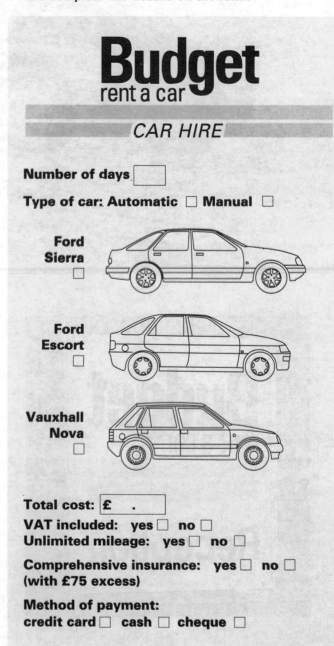

Budget
rent a car

CAR HIRE

Number of days ☐

Type of car: Automatic ☐ **Manual** ☐

Ford Sierra ☐

Ford Escort ☐

Vauxhall Nova ☐

	TRUE	FALSE
a) David doesn't want to drive Paola down to Cornwall.	☐	☐
b) Paola doesn't want David to drive her down to Cornwall.	☐	☐
c) The magazine is paying for the car hire.	☐	☐
d) David is seeing Paola at the weekend.	☐	☐
e) David wants to get some cigarettes.	☐	☐
f) David will be back in about five minutes.	☐	☐

Total cost: £   .

VAT included: yes ☐ no ☐

Unlimited mileage: yes ☐ no ☐

Comprehensive insurance: yes ☐ no ☐
(with £75 excess)

Method of payment:
credit card ☐ **cash** ☐ **cheque** ☐

▶ **Watch and check. Correct the false sentences.**

SECTION TWO

(to the end)

>> **FOCUS ON LANGUAGE** <<
polite requests

1 First fill in the gaps with words and phrases from the box.

> If you could just (×2)   Could I see
> if that's possible   I'd like to
> Could you give me   please

Paola: _ _ _ _ _ _ _ _ _ _ leave the car at Heathrow Airport, _ _ _ _ _ _ _ _ _ _ ?

Clerk: That's no problem. But there's an additional charge of £50.

Paola: OK.

Clerk: _ _ _ _ _ _ _ _ _ _ your driving licence, _ _ _ _ _ _ _ _ _ _ ? Thank you. _ _ _ _ _ _ _ _ _ _ a local contact address?

Paola: Yes. I'm staying at the Old Custom House Hotel, Padstow, in Cornwall.

Clerk: Do you know the telephone number?

Paola: No, I'm afraid I don't.

Clerk: That's OK. Right, the amount here is left blank until you return. The petrol tank is full when you start. If you return it full, no extra charge is made. OK, _ _ _ _ _ _ _ _ _ _ sign here. If you get any parking tickets or speeding fines, you have to pay them yourself. You mustn't take the vehicle outside the UK. _ _ _ _ _ _ _ _ _ _ sign here … and here.

>> **Watch and check.**

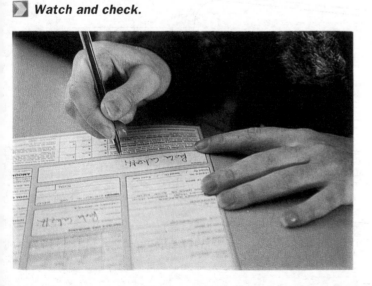

2 Put the sentences in the correct order to make a conversation.

☐	Very funny, David!
☐	Any time.
1	We drive on the left, don't forget.
☐	OK. And thanks for dinner last night, it was lovely.
☐	Bye. Safe journey.
☐	I'll see you on Saturday. Call me when you get to the hotel.
☐	Goodbye.

>> **Watch and check.**

Review

Are these sentences true or false? Correct the false ones.

		TRUE	FALSE
1	David is going to Cornwall at the weekend.	☐	☐
2	David goes into the car hire office with Paola.	☐	☐
3	Paola says she wants a large car.	☐	☐
4	There's an excess of £75 on the insurance.	☐	☐
5	Paola would like to leave the car at Gatwick Airport.	☐	☐
6	Paola doesn't know the phone number of the hotel in Cornwall.	☐	☐
7	The petrol tank is full when she starts.	☐	☐
8	The car hire company has to pay any parking tickets or speeding fines.	☐	☐

After you watch

Summary

CUSTOMER

I'd like to hire a car.
I'd like to leave the car at Heathrow Airport, if that's possible.

CAR HIRE CLERK

Can I help you?
What size of car would you like?
Would you like an automatic or a manual?
I'd recommend a Ford Escort.
For four days that would be £150.
That includes …
How would you like to pay?
Could I see your driving licence, please?
Could you give me a local contact address?
If you could just sign here.
Have a safe journey.

ACTIVITY ONE

Role-play: HIRING A CAR

Student A: the customer

You want to hire a car. Decide whether you're travelling alone or with someone else, and what size of car you want, automatic or manual. Also decide how you want to pay and where you want to leave the car. Your local contact address is The Queen's Hotel, Hastings, tel: 0424 96325.

Student B: car hire clerk

Student A comes into your office. Ask if you can help. Use the information on the right to recommend a car. Then fill in the form below.

INFORMATION

Small cars
Ford Escort 1.4 (manual)
£37.50 per day. £225 per week.

Rover Metro 1.1 (automatic)
£35 per day. £210 per week.

Large cars
Rover 800 (manual)
£50 per day. £300 per week.

Ford Sierra 2.0 (automatic)
£50 per day. £300 per week.

All prices include:

VAT

Unlimited mileage

*Comprehensive insurance
(with £100 excess)*

Additional charge for leaving the car at another hire office: £75

CAR HIRE AGREEMENT

Car   Make   Model

        Manual   Automatic

Number of days ___ at £ ___ per day

        £   p
    Cost
Additional charge
    Total cost

Method of payment:
    Visa   cheque
    American Express   Access
    cash

Local contact address: _____

Telephone No: _____

Signature of driver:

ACTIVITY TWO

Label the pictures using words from the box. Use your dictionary if you want to.

windscreen   wheel   door
gear stick   clutch   brake pedal
accelerator pedal   handbrake   aerial
bonnet   boot   steering-wheel

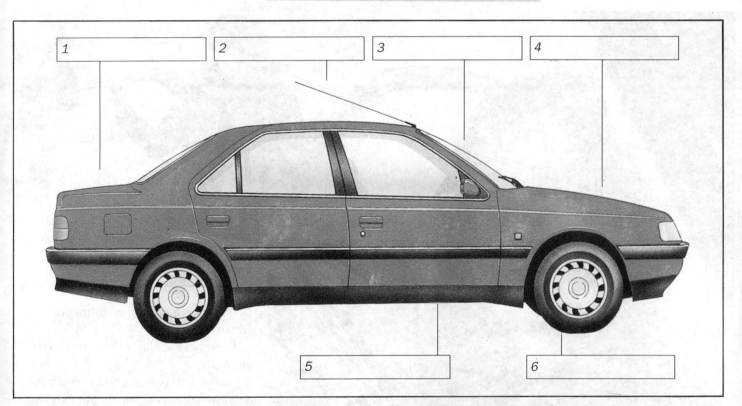

1
2
3
4
5
6

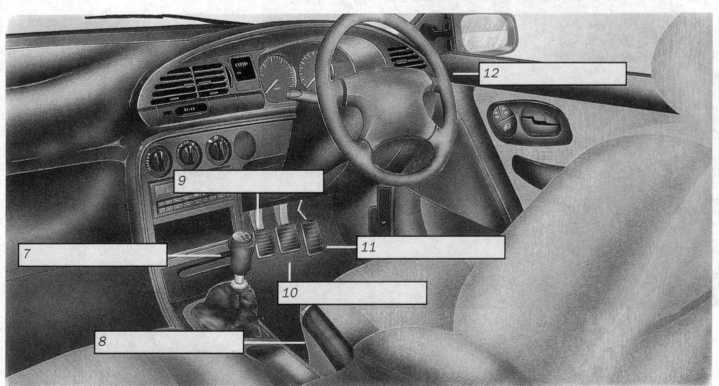

12
9
7
11
10
8

4 PURPLE VIOLIN

Before you watch

Do you play a musical instrument? If so, which one?

Did you have lessons or did you teach yourself?

Do you often see buskers? Do you stop and listen? Do you give them money? Would you ever go out busking?

1 Fill in the gaps using words from the below.

influenced	painting	strings
record store	inherited	piece

a) Haydn _ _ _ _ _ Beethoven. Beethoven's early music
   sounds like Haydn.

b) Ed was a painter. He studied _ _ _ _ _ at art college.

c) 'Where did you get that old violin?'

   'I _ _ _ _ _ it from my grandfather.'

d) Vivaldi's *The Four Seasons* is a beautiful _ _ _ _ _ of music.

e) I bought this CD at the _ _ _ _ _ in town.

f) There are four _ _ _ _ _ on a violin.

**2 Label the pictures using words from the box
on the right.**

one-man band	violin	double bass
viola	cello	steel band	electric guitar

a) _ _ _ _ _

b) _ _ _ _ _

c) _ _ _ _ _

d) _ _ _ _ _

e) _ _ _ _ _

f) _ _ _ _ _

g) _ _ _ _ _

3 Match the words with the correct definitions.

1 improvise (v)

2 imitate (v)

3 melody (n)

4 composer (n)

5 combine (v)

6 device (n)

7 carry on (v)

8 folk band (n)

a) tune

b) continue

c) a small machine (with
    a special purpose)

d) compose or play music
    without preparing it first

e) copy

f) a group of musicians who
    play in the traditional style
    of a country or region

g) put (things) together; join

h) a person who writes music

While you watch

▶ **Watch the whole video and tick the correct boxes.**

1 Ed Alleyne-Johnson ☐ enjoyed ☐ didn't enjoy playing classical music at school.

2 He studied ☐ music ☐ painting at college.

3 He started playing on the streets in England and then travelled around ☐ Europe ☐ Europe and the States ☐ the States.

4 Ed's violin has got ☐ three ☐ four ☐ five strings.

5 ☐ Ed built his violin himself.
   ☐ Ed bought his violin.

6 Ed has sold ☐ 3,000 ☐ 13,000 ☐ 30,000 copies of his CD so far.

7 Ed is going to ☐ carry on busking ☐ stop busking.

SECTION ONE

(*to* **Ed:** … it's back to the drawing-board.)

≫   **FOCUS ON LANGUAGE**   ≪
              verb patterns

1 Underline the correct verb forms.

Ed: I learnt *play/to play/playing* the violin at school. I played in the school orchestra, but I didn't really enjoy *play/to play/playing* classical music. It was too rigid. You have to *play/to play/playing* exactly what the composer wrote, and I wanted *experiment/to experiment* and to improvise, and write my own music.

Michael: So, did you go to music college?

Ed: No, I studied painting at the School of Drawing and Fine Art in Oxford. But I carried on *play/to play/playing* the violin in rock bands and folk bands.

Michael: So, what did you do when you left college?

Ed: I tried *make/to make* a career as a painter, but it was too difficult, so I went back to music.

Michael: And that's when you started *busk/busking*?

Ed: That's right. I started *play/playing* on the streets in England, and then I travelled round Europe and the States.

▶ **Watch and check.**

2 Are these sentences true or false? ▶ Watch and check your answers, then correct the false sentences.

	TRUE	FALSE
a) Ed met a lot of different musicians in Europe and the States.	☐	☐
b) Ed plays a Breton melody for Michael.	☐	☐
c) European music didn't influence Ed's music.	☐	☐
d) Ed busks more than he used to.	☐	☐
e) When Ed writes a new tune, he takes it out on the street and plays it to people.	☐	☐

SECTION TWO

(*to* **Ed:** It's a sort of trade mark.)

Ed's electric violin

Ed's first violin

> **Watch the video and answer these questions.**

1 Why is Ed's electric violin like a violin and a viola built into one?

– –

2 Where did Ed get his first violin?

– –

3 Why did he paint his first violin purple?

– –

4 Why did he paint his electric violin purple?

– –

SECTION THREE

(*to* **Ed:** It's a sort of high-tech, one-man band.)

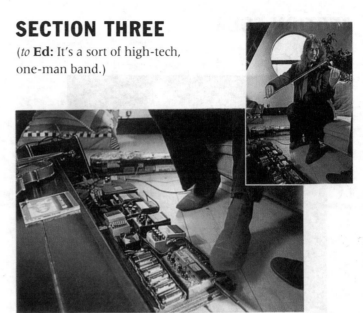

Look at this diagram of Ed's equipment.

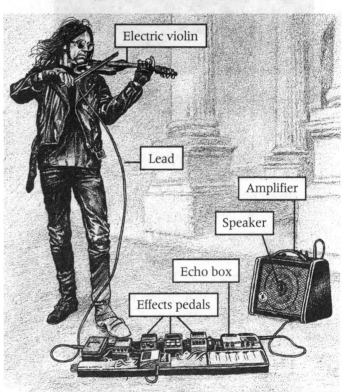

Electric violin

Lead

Amplifier

Speaker

Echo box

Effects pedals

> **Watch the video and answer these questions.**

1 What do the special effects pedals do?

– –

– –

2 What does the echo box do?

– –

SECTION FOUR
(*to the end*)

1 Put these sentences in the correct order to make a conversation.

1	So, you've also made a CD, haven't you?
	So, you did it all yourself?
	About 30,000 so far.
	That's right. It's called 'The Purple Electric Violin Concerto' for obvious reasons. It was very cheap to make. Because of the way I work, I can record straight onto digital tape instead of having to use a big recording studio. Digital tape's a sort of high-quality cassette that enables you to make a CD.
	That's right. Because there isn't a big record company behind it, I was free to record whatever I wanted.
	So, how many copies have you sold?

▶ **Watch and check.**

2 What are Ed's plans for the future?

3 Discuss these questions.

a) What do you think of Ed's music? Do you like it? Why/Why not?

b) Would you buy a CD of it?

Review

Complete this summary using the words and phrases in the box.

> composer and violinist
>
> is now recording another
>
> busking
>
> wanted to improvise
>
> he was at school
>
> tried to become a painter
>
> inherited his first violin
>
> as a C string on a viola
>
> playing classical music
>
> to make it look nicer
>
> to stop busking
>
> repaired it

Ed Alleyne-Johnson is a
_ _ _ _ _ _ _ _ _ _ . He started
playing the violin when
_ _ _ _ _ _ _ _ _ _ , but he
didn't enjoy _ _ _ _ _ _ _ _ _ _ .
He _ _ _ _ _ _ _ _ _ _ and
write his own music. When
he left art college, he
_ _ _ _ _ _ _ _ _ _ . But it
was too difficult, so he
went back to music. He
started _ _ _ _ _ _ _ _ _ _ and travelled
around Europe and the States.
Ed _ _ _ _ _ _ _ _ _ _ from his grandfather. It was broken, so
he _ _ _ _ _ _ _ _ _ _ and painted it purple _ _ _ _ _ _ _ _ _ _ .
He built his second violin himself. It has five strings: the
bottom string is the same _ _ _ _ _ _ _ _ _ _ .
Ed has made a CD and _ _ _ _ _ _ _ _ _ _ – but he's not
going _ _ _ _ _ _ _ _ _ _ !

After you watch

ACTIVITY ONE

1 Read the advertisement for the music club. Are these sentences true or false?

	TRUE	FALSE
a) You can choose a CD by Bruce Springsteen.	☐	☐
b) You can choose 3 CDs for £14.99.	☐	☐
c) You can keep the CDs for 10 days before you pay for them.	☐	☐
d) You will receive a free CD rack and a CD cleaner when you join the club.	☐	☐
e) You do not need a stamp when you send the form.	☐	☐
f) The total cost, including post and packing, is £20.99.	☐	☐
g) When you join the club, you agree to buy 12 CDs during the next two years.	☐	☐

2 Work in pairs. Decide together which CDs you will order. Then discuss your choice with another pair.

MARATHON MUSIC CLUB

3 Compact Discs free! when you buy just one!

Join our club now! Save £££s!
Choose any four compact discs and you'll only pay the price of one. That's just £14.99 for 4 discs!

10 day trial
You can keep the CDs for 10 days – if you don't like them, simply send them back to us. Do not send any money now.

Free gift
If you join our club now, we will send you a free CD rack or a CD cleaner.

Club magazine
Every month we'll send you our free club magazine. You can choose your favourite music and we'll send it to your home. No need to go to the shops!
Fill in this form and send it to:
Marathon Music Club, FREEPOST, P.O. Box 98, Middleton, Sussex.
You don't need a stamp!

YES! Please accept me as a member and send me these four compact discs for the incredibly low price of £14.99 (plus £6 post and packing).

Write the numbers in the boxes. ☐ ☐ ☐ ☐

Please also send me my free gift! Tick one box for your free gift. ☐ CD rack ☐
CD cleaner
If I am not completely satisfied, I will send back all four CDs within 10 days and I will owe nothing. If I keep the CDs I will send £20.99 to Marathon Club.
Please send me my monthly magazine. I do not have to buy a CD every month, but I agree to buy at least 10 CDs during the next two years.

Mr/Mrs/Miss/Ms_____

Address_____

_____ Postcode _____

Signature_____

You must sign the form or we cannot send you the CDs. If we cannot send you the CDs you want, you can choose different ones. Please allow up to 28 days for delivery. Offer applies in UK only. Only one membership per household.

You may receive advertisements for other products. Please tick this box if you do not want to receive them. ☐

01 REM Automatic for the people
02 Michael Jackson Dangerous
03 Abba Greatest Hits
04 The Beatles Sergeant Pepper
05 Ed Alleyne-Johnson Purple Electric Violin Concerto
06 Eric Clapton Unplugged
07 Phil Collins Serious Hits ... Live!
08 Dire Straits Making Movies
09 Simply Red Greatest Hits
10 The Eagles Hotel California
11 Eurythmics Greatest Hits
12 Jimi Hendrix The Ultimate Experience
13 David Bowie Singles Collection
14 Elton John Goodbye Yellow Brick Road
15 Madonna Immaculate Collection

16 Bob Marley Greatest Hits
17 Elvis Presley From the Heart
18 Queen Greatest Hits
19 Prince The Hits 1
20 Pink Floyd The Dark Side of the Moon
21 The Rolling Stones Rolled Gold
22 Police Greatest Hits
23 Diana Ross One Woman – the Ultimate Collection
24 Love Songs A collection of the best love songs
25 Simon and Garfunkel Sounds of Silence
26 U2 Greatest Hits
27 Rod Stewart Greatest Hits
28 UB40 Promises and Lies
29 Tina Turner What's Love got to do with it?
30 Bruce Springsteen Born in the USA
31 10CC Greatest Hits
32 Supertramp Even in the Quietest Moments
33 Frank Sinatra Duets
34 Ella Fitzgerald Songs
35 ACDC Greatest Hits

ACTIVITY TWO

DESERT ISLAND DISCS

You are going to a desert island, and you are allowed to take a cassette player with you. But you can only take one cassette with *three* pieces of music on it. Which three pieces of music will you take?

Discuss your choice with a partner.

Situation

5 ▷ THE HOTEL

Before you watch

Have you ever stayed in a hotel?
What kind of hotel was it?
Do you like staying in hotels? /Would you like to stay in a hotel?
Have you ever made a complaint in a hotel?

Look at these photographs. What do you think happens? What are the people saying to each other?

While you watch

▶ **Watch the whole video and check your ideas for the photographs above.**

SECTION ONE

(to **Paola:** Thank you. *After the receptionist has brought the towels.*)

Fill in the gaps in the conversation.

Receptionist: Reception.

Paola: Yes, hello. This is Paola Calvetti in room 10. _ _ _ _ _ _ _ _ _ there aren't _ _ _ _ _ _ _ _ _ in the bathroom.

Receptionist: Oh, I'm _ _ _ _ _ _ _ _ _ _. I'll _ _ _ _ _ _ _ _ _ _ up right away.

Paola: Come in.

Receptionist: _ _ _ _ _ _ _ _ _ your towels. I do _ _ _ _ _. The chambermaid forgot to leave them.

Paola: It _ _ _ _ _ matter, really. Don't _ _ _ _ _ .

Receptionist: _ _ _ _ _ you are. Is _ _ _ _ _ else OK?

Paola: Yes, it's _ _ _ _ _ .

Receptionist: _ _ _ _ _, I hope you _ _ _ _ _ your stay.

Paola: _ _ _ _ _ you.

▶ **Watch and check.**

SECTION TWO

(*to the end*)

Look at the phone conversation between Paola and David. What do you think David's questions are?

David: Hello. David Evans here.

Paola: Hi, it's me.

David: Hi. You've arrived then.

Paola: Yes, I checked in a few minutes ago.

David: _ .

Paola: Oh, it's on the sea front. It's quite small, but it's very clean and comfortable. I have a wonderful view of the harbour from my window. It's a beautiful village, David. It's very peaceful and quiet.

David: _ .

Paola: Oh, not too bad. I got stuck in a traffic jam near Exeter, but I wasn't held up for long.

David: _ .

Paola: David!

David: Sorry.

Paola: When are you coming down?

David: On Friday night. _ .

Paola: Yes, let's do that.

David: _ .

Paola: It's very easy to find. It's on the harbour.

David: OK. I'll see you on Saturday, then. Be good.

Paola: Yes, OK. Bye.

David: Bye.

▶ **Watch and check.**

Review

Fill in the gaps in the summary using verbs from the box. Put them in the past simple.

arrive	arrange	ring (×2)	check in
describe	bring	have	put
discover	wash	go	

Paola _ _ _ _ _ at the hotel in Padstow, and _ _ _ _ _ . The receptionist _ _ _ _ _ her in room 10, which _ _ _ _ _ a wonderful view of the harbour.

Paola _ _ _ _ _ into the bathroom and _ _ _ _ _ her hands. Then she _ _ _ _ _ that there were no towels. She _ _ _ _ _ reception to complain, and the receptionist _ _ _ _ _ up some towels. Then Paola _ _ _ _ _ David in Bath. She _ _ _ _ _ the hotel and the village, and they _ _ _ _ _ to meet on Saturday.

After you watch

Summary

MAKING A COMPLAINT
I'm afraid there isn't / aren't any …
It doesn't matter, really.
Don't worry.

APOLOGIZING
I'm terribly sorry. I'll bring some up right away.
I do apologize.
Is everything else OK?

OFFERING/DECLINING HELP
Shall I get somebody to help you with your bags?
No, thank you. I can manage.

ROOM SERVICE
Could I have a coffee to room 10, please?
Certainly, madam. It'll be about ten minutes.

ANSWERING THE PHONE AT WORK
Good afternoon. Bath Herald.
Hello. David Evans here.
Reception.
Room service.

ACTIVITY ONE
Role-play: MAKING A COMPLAINT

Student A: Hotel guest
You have just checked in at a hotel and gone to your room. Choose one of the problems below and ring reception to complain.
- There's no soap.
- There's no toilet paper.
- The TV doesn't work.
- The bedside light doesn't work.
- The carpet's dirty.

Student B: Receptionist
You are a hotel receptionist. Student A has just checked in and gone to their room. They ring up to complain about something. Apologize and deal with the problem.

ACTIVITY TWO
Role-play: ORDERING FROM ROOM SERVICE

Student A: Hotel guest
You are in your room at a hotel. Ring room service and order from the room service menu.

Student B: Waiter/waitress
Student A rings you with a room service order. Take the order and tell them how long it will be.

ROOM SERVICE MENU	
Breakfast	
Continental breakfast (fruit juice, toast or croissants, tea or coffee)	£6.50
English breakfast (fruit juice, cereal, eggs, bacon, sausage, tomato, toast, tea or coffee)	£8.00
Cold snacks	£3.25
Sandwiches (tuna, ham, beef, cheese and tomato)	£2.50
Plate of cakes and pastries	
Hot snacks	£4.00
Beefburger (with onions, in a roll)	£3.50
Toasted sandwiches (ham, cheese, cheese and tomato)	£1.75
French fries	
Drinks	£1.70
Coffee (per pot for one person)	£1.50
Tea (per pot for one person)	£1.20
Fruit juice (orange, tomato, grapefruit, apple)	£1.20
Canned drinks (Cola, fizzy orange)	£1.90
Hot chocolate	

ACTIVITY THREE

Label this picture of a hotel room using words from the box. Use a dictionary if necessary.

wardrobe   bed   bedside table   lamp
armchair   television   chair   curtains
mirror   chest of drawers   dressing table

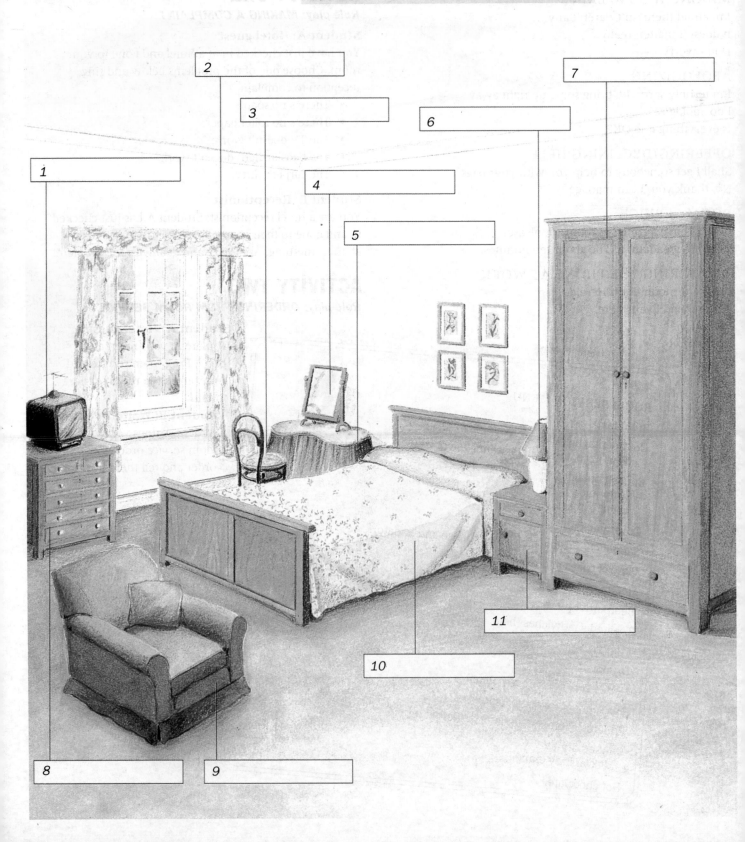

6 ▷ WALES

PÊL DROED

Rwyf yn chwarae pêl droed i dim pêl droed dan 10, Llanberis. Dydd Sadwrn mae gennym ni'r gêm gyntaf yn erbyn Cae Gwyn, Caernarfon. Rydym yn gwisgo shorts du, gwyn a choch, sanau coch a chrys coch. Gwilym sydd yn ein hyfforddi ni.

Before you watch

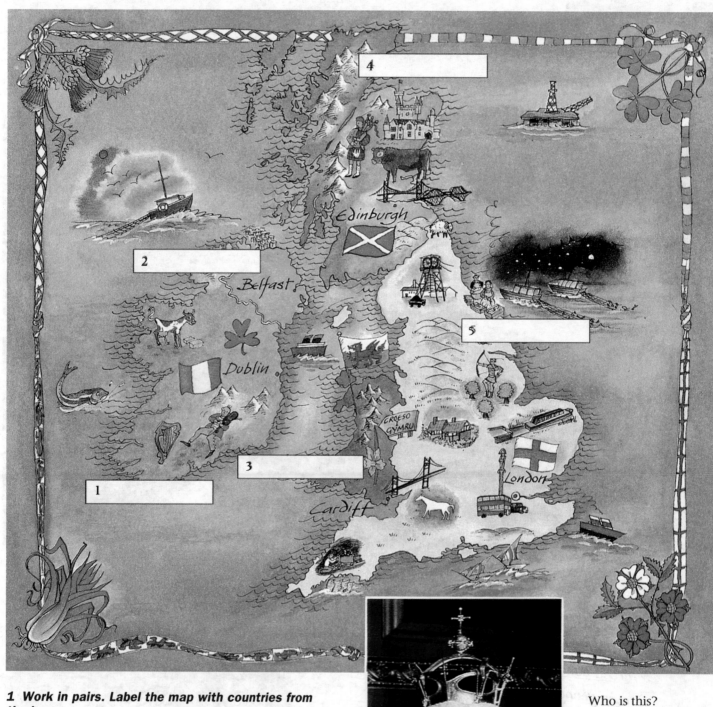

1 Work in pairs. Label the map with countries from the box.

Scotland   Wales   England
The Republic of Ireland   Northern Ireland

Which of the five countries belong to the United Kingdom?
How many languages are spoken in the British Isles?
Where are they spoken?
How many languages are spoken in your country?

Who is this?
What is his full title?

2 Read the information about North Wales. Fill in the gaps using words from the box.

bilingual	castles	nation
scenery	flag	Celtic
invaded	highest	

North Wales

Caernarfon

▲ Mount Snowdon

In North Wales you can see some of the most beautiful _ _ _ _ _ in Britain. Take a train to the top of Snowdon, Wales' _ _ _ _ **mountain.**

This is the Welsh _ _ _ _ _ _. Although Wales is not an independent _ _ _ _ _, it has its own culture and language.

Welsh is a _ _ _ _ _ language and one of the oldest in Europe. Many people in Wales are _ _ _ _ _ : they speak Welsh as their first language.

Key:

70% of the people speak Welsh

Cardiff

There are many huge _ _ _ _ _ in North Wales. The English built them in the thirteenth century when they _ _ _ _ _ Wales.

Here are some Welsh words and phrases that you can use if you visit North Wales

Bore da.	Good morning.
Sut ydych chi?	How are you?
Iawn, diolch.	Fine, thanks.
os gwelwch yn dda	please
diolch	thank you

While you watch

Read these sentences.

1 ☐ In 1292
   ☐ In 1092 Edward I invaded Wales.

2 The first Prince of Wales was called ☐ Edward.
                                         ☐ Charles.

3 The ☐ Welsh   have ruled ☐ England for many centuries.
       ☐ English   ☐ Wales

4 Eighty-six per cent of the people in Llanberis speak
   ☐ Welsh   as their first language.
   ☐ English

5 There are ☐ fewer   silent letters in English than in Welsh.
             ☐ more

6 Welsh has survived for more than ☐ 200 years.
                                     ☐ 2,000 years.
                                     ☐ 1,000 years.

7 ☐ Very few   people believe that Welsh should be preserved.
   ☐ Many

▶ **Watch the whole video and choose the correct alternative.**

SECTION ONE

(to **Amanda:** Prince Charles became the … Prince of Wales.)

Try to fill in the gaps with the numbers from the box.

fourteen	twenty-first	half
second	two and three quarter million	

1 Wales is about _ _ _ _ _ the size of Switzerland.
2 It has a population of _ _ _ _ _ _ .
3 Snowdon is Britain's _ _ _ _ _ highest mountain.
4 Edward I built _ _ _ _ _ huge castles to control the Welsh people.
5 Prince Charles is the _ _ _ _ _ Prince of Wales.

▶ **Watch the video and check your answers.**

SECTION TWO

(up to the end of the interviews with the schoolchildren)

1 ❯ **Watch the video and tick the signs that you see.**

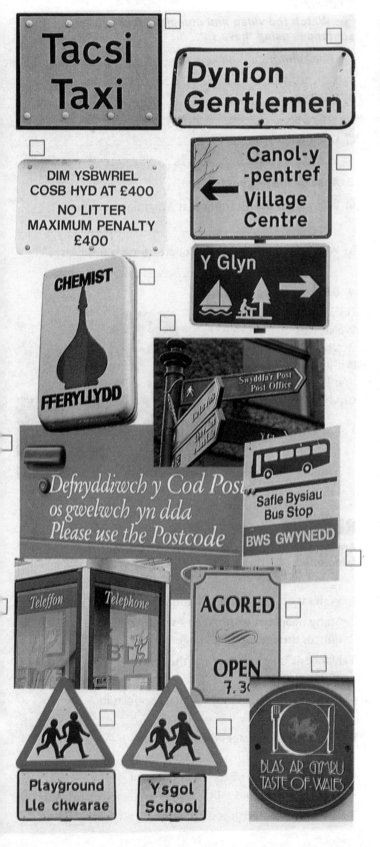

2 *Fill in the gaps using words from the box.*

Elizabeth Roberts,
Headmistress of Llanberis Primary School

> Welsh   folk tales   cultures
> language policy   English   pick up
> learns   languages   bilingual

Ms Roberts: The _ _ _ _ _ in the school is that children
  should be _ _ _ _ _ by the time that they are eleven years
  old. The children are taught through the medium of
  _ _ _ _ _ most of the time, but we do teach _ _ _ _ _ to
  them as well.

Amanda: Is it a problem for them learning two _ _ _ _ _
  instead of one?

Ms Roberts: No, not at all. What happens when a child
  _ _ _ _ _ two languages at the same time is that they have
  an insight into two _ _ _ _ _. They learn to read, so they
  have all the _ _ _ _ _ of two languages. And another thing
  that helps them is that they can _ _ _ _ _ the third and
  fourth language without any problem at all.

❯ **Watch and check.**

3 *Do you agree with Elizabeth Roberts? Discuss
these questions.*

a) Are there any other advantages in being
   bilingual?
b) Are there any disadvantages?
c) Is it true that people who already speak two
   languages find it very easy to learn a third
   and fourth language?

SECTION THREE

(to the end)

1 Answer these questions.

a) Which of these are Celtic languages?

☐ English   ☐ Scottish Gaelic

☐ Welsh   ☐ French

☐ Irish Gaelic   ☐ Breton

b) Where are Celtic languages still spoken today? Mark the areas on the map.

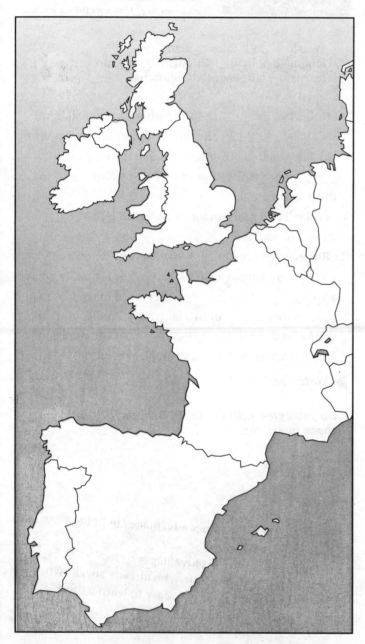

c) What percentage of Welsh people now speak Welsh?

_ _ _ _

▶ **Watch and check.**

2 What are people doing to preserve the Welsh language?

▶ **Watch the video and complete these three sentences using 'have to'.**

a) Official forms and documents _

b) Road signs _

c) Children at school _

3 Answer these questions.

a) What is the fourth thing that Amanda mentions?

_ _

b) What else does Elizabeth Roberts think is necessary?

_ _

4 Discuss these questions.

Do you think Welsh will survive? Is it important that Welsh survives?

REVIEW

Are these sentences true or false? Correct the false ones.

	TRUE	FALSE
1 Wales is an independent nation.	☐	☐
2 Many people in North Wales speak English only as their second language.	☐	☐
3 Llanberis is a small town at the foot of Snowdon.	☐	☐
4 Welsh is the only Celtic language spoken in the British Isles.	☐	☐
5 Most Celtic languages died out a long time ago.	☐	☐
6 Over the last 100 years the number of Welsh speakers has fallen slowly.	☐	☐
7 The future of Welsh is uncertain.	☐	☐

After you watch

ACTIVITY ONE

You are going to read an article about why the number of Welsh-speakers has declined so quickly over the last 100 years.

1 Read the article quickly and put these paragraph headings into the correct places in the text.

Industrialization   The media   Education
Rural depopulation   Holiday homes

THE DECLINE OF WELSH

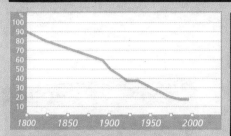

A HUNDRED years ago 60% of Welsh people spoke Welsh. Now only 20% are Welsh-speaking. Why have the numbers fallen so quickly? Here are some of the reasons for the decline.

In the nineteenth century people thought that Welsh was an uncivilized language.

If you wanted to be successful in life, you had to learn English, the language of the British Empire. So in many schools in Wales the children were forbidden to speak Welsh.

At the beginning of the twentieth century many English and Irish people moved to South Wales to work in the coal mines and steel works. They didn't learn Welsh.

People, especially young people, moved away from the Welsh-speaking villages and farms of north and west Wales to look for work in the big towns and cities, so the Welsh-speaking communities became much smaller.

In the 1960s and 1970s many English people bought holiday cottages in villages in Wales. Most of them did not learn Welsh. This also pushed up the price of houses so that local Welsh-speaking people couldn't afford them.

English comes into every Welsh home through the television, the radio, newspapers, books, etc. There are Welsh-language TV and radio stations, but far fewer than English ones. And now there's cable and satellite TV, too – in English, of course!

The decline in the number of Welsh speakers has now stopped. But will numbers ever start to increase again? Young people are now learning Welsh in school, but if the small Welsh-speaking communities of North Wales die, then the Welsh language will probably not survive as a living language.

2 Read the article again and answer these questions.

a) What percentage of the Welsh population spoke Welsh in 1800?

b) Why were children forbidden to speak Welsh in school in the nineteenth century?

c) Why did many English and Irish people move to south Wales in the early twentieth century?

d) Why did people move away from north and west Wales? What was the result of this?

e) Who bought holiday cottages in Welsh villages in the 1960s and 1970s?

f) What happened to house prices in villages?

g) Are there more Welsh-language TV and radio stations in Wales than English-language ones?

h) What will happen if Welsh-speaking communities in North Wales die?

ACTIVITY TWO
Discussion

Should we protect 'minority languages'? Why?/Why not?
Are there any minority languages in your country?
Are people working to preserve them? If so, how are they
doing this?

ACTIVITY THREE
Where are these languages spoken? Work in pairs or groups and put them in the correct box.

French	Breton	Galician	Frisian
Romansch	German	Italian	Flemish
Basque	Catalan	Spanish	

SPAIN	FRANCE	GERMANY
ITALY	BELGIUM	SWITZERLAND

7 ▷ BBC WORLD SERVICE

Before you watch

Do you listen to the radio?

What stations do you listen to?

What kind of programmes do you like?

Have you ever listened to the BBC World Service?

What do the letters BBC stand for?

Work in pairs. Read the information about the BBC World Service and fill in the gaps using words from the box.

announcer	true	propaganda
reputation	broadcasts	bulletins
colonies	journalists	headquarters

Bush House, _ _ _ _ _ _ of the BBC World Service.

History

The BBC World Service began in 1932. Then, it was called the Empire Service. It broadcast news programmes in English to people living in the British _ _ _ _ _ , such as India, Kenya, or the West Indies. In the Second World War it started broadcasting in other languages to counteract fascist _ _ _ _ _ _ from Germany and Italy.

An _ _ _ _ _ _ reading the news

NEWS ... NEWS ... NEWS

Around 120 _ _ _ _ _ _ work in the newsroom. Each day they write 200 news _ _ _ _ _ _ . Each news story is checked at least twice to make sure that it is _ _ _ _ _ _ .

- The BBC is the world's largest international broadcaster.
- The BBC World Service _ _ _ _ _ _ 24 hours a day in 39 languages.
- 130 million people listen to the World Service every week.
- People listen to the BBC because of its _ _ _ _ _ for honesty and accuracy.

While you watch

Match the sentences to the pictures. Then
watch the whole video and check.

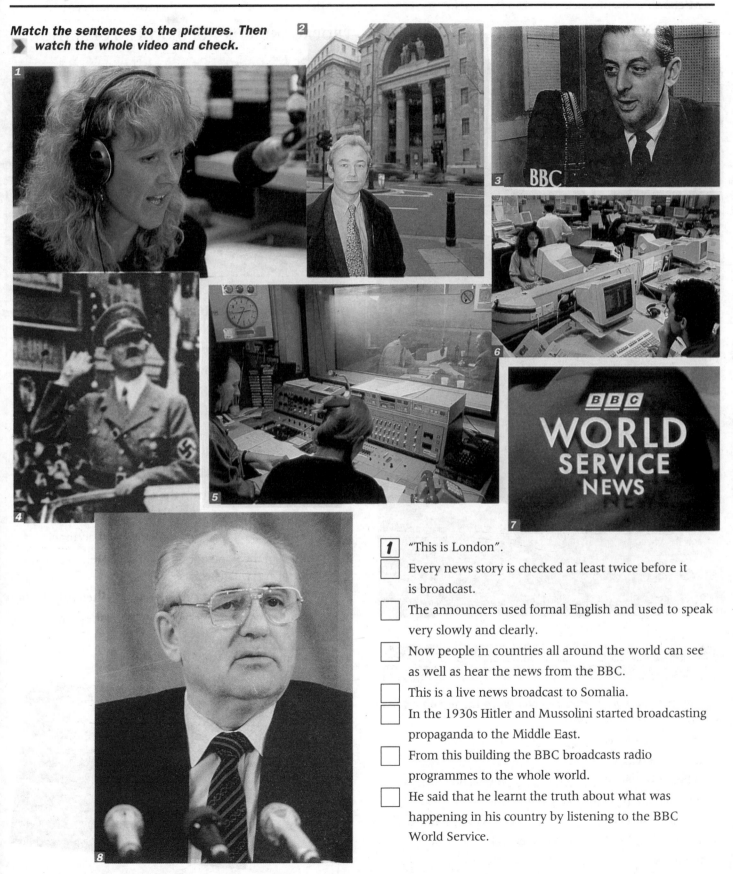

1	"This is London".
	Every news story is checked at least twice before it is broadcast.
	The announcers used formal English and used to speak very slowly and clearly.
	Now people in countries all around the world can see as well as hear the news from the BBC.
	This is a live news broadcast to Somalia.
	In the 1930s Hitler and Mussolini started broadcasting propaganda to the Middle East.
	From this building the BBC broadcasts radio programmes to the whole world.
	He said that he learnt the truth about what was happening in his country by listening to the BBC World Service.

SECTION ONE

(*to* **Michael:** … dinner-jackets to read the news.)

THE EARLY DAYS

>> **FOCUS ON LANGUAGE** <<
used to

> **Watch the video and then complete these sentences using 'used to' and a verb.**

1 The World Service _ _ _ _ _ _ _ _ _ _ called 'The Empire Service'.

2 When it started, it _ _ _ _ _ _ _ _ _ _ news and information to people living in the British colonies.

3 The announcers _ _ _ _ _ _ _ _ _ _ very slowly and clearly.

4 They _ _ _ _ _ _ _ _ _ _ into dinner-jackets to read the news.

SECTION TWO

(*to* **Michael:** … information in their own country.)

PROPAGANDA OR ACCURATE INFORMATION?

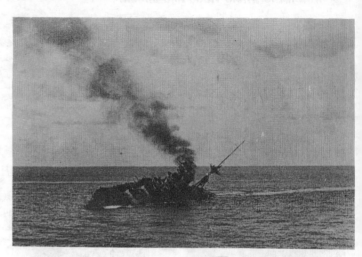

Tick the correct alternative, then > **watch the video and check your answers.**

1 In 1938 the BBC started broadcasting to the Middle East

☐   a) to counteract the influence of fascist propaganda.

☐   b) to teach English to people living there.

☐   c) to counteract the influence of Arab propaganda.

2 During the Second World War the BBC reported British defeats as well as British victories, so

☐   a) it wasn't popular with the British Government.

☐   b) it was popular with the German and Italian Governments.

☐   c) it got a reputation for honesty and accuracy.

3 Over 40% of the population in Somalia listen to the news broadcasts every day because

☐   a) there aren't any radio stations in their own country.

☐   b) they cannot get accurate news and information in their own country.

☐   c) they like to listen to the news in English.

SECTION THREE

(to the end)

THE NEWSROOM

1 ▷ *Watch the video and answer these questions.*

   a) What happens in the Newsroom?

   _____

   _____

   b) How did President Gorbachev find out what was
       happening in his country when he was under house
       arrest in 1991?

   _____

   _____

   c) Why did the former Soviet Union jam BBC broadcasts
       for many years?

   _____

   _____

   d) What made the British Government very angry
       in 1956?

   _____

   _____

   e) What did the BBC World Service do in 1992?

   _____

   _____

2 What do you think?

What radio broadcasting companies are there in
your country?
What kinds of programme do they broadcast?
Do they broadcast in any other languages?

Review

**There are five mistakes in this summary. Find them and
correct them.**

The World Service started in 1922. When it began, it
broadcast in English and Arabic and provided news and
information to people living in the British colonies.
In the 1930s Hitler and Mussolini started broadcasting news
bulletins to the Middle East, so in 1938 Britain also began
broadcasting to the Middle East – in Arabic.
During the Second World War the BBC only reported
British defeats so it got a reputation for honesty
and accuracy.
Journalists in the Newsroom write 200 news bulletins
every week. Every news story is checked at least twice
after it is broadcast. The BBC will only broadcast
accurate information.

After you watch

ACTIVITY ONE

1 Read the text and answer these questions.

a) What were the three aims of the BBC?

b) What was the big discussion about?

c) Who controlled the radio companies in the Soviet Union?

d) Did the American broadcasting companies produce high-quality programmes?

e) Who thought that the British Government should control the BBC?

f) Can the British Government tell the BBC what to broadcast?

g) Is the BBC still a monopoly?

h) Where does the BBC get money from?

WHO CONTROLS THE BBC?

The BBC began in 1922. Of course, in those days there was no television, only radio. The BBC had three aims: to educate, to inform, and to entertain.

At first there was a big discussion about who should control the BBC. Should it be independent or should it be controlled by the government? People in Britain looked at broadcasting companies in other countries. In the Soviet Union, for example, the radio companies were controlled by the government and had to broadcast exactly what the government wanted – usually political propaganda. By contrast, in the USA there was no government control at all. There were dozens of private broadcasting companies, but they were badly organized, the programmes were of low quality, and there were advertisements ('commercial breaks') in the programmes.

Many British politicians – Winston Churchill, for example – thought that the British Government should have complete control of the BBC. Others thought Britain should follow the American example. But they finally reached a compromise and decided that

- the British Government should own the BBC;
- the BBC should be politically neutral and independent (the government should not tell the BBC what to broadcast);
- the BBC should be a monopoly (no-one else was allowed to broadcast programmes. This changed in the 1950s);
- the BBC should receive money from the sale of licences (everybody who owned a radio or television had to buy a licence).

2 Discuss these questions.

How many broadcasting companies are there in your country?

Who controls them?

Where do they get money from?

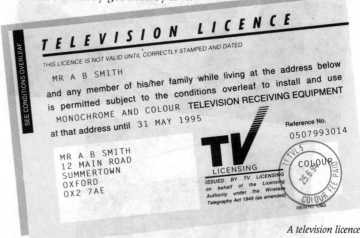

A television licence

ACTIVITY TWO

1 Look at the radio programmes opposite and answer these questions.

a) Which programme is after Waveguide?

b) In which programme can you hear about the arts?

c) Which programme is before Multitrack 3?

d) What can you hear at 10.15?

e) Which sporting event can you hear about in Sportsworld?

f) How many times can you hear the news?

2 Work in pairs. Choose three programmes to listen to.

RADIO PROGRAMMES

SATURDAYS

All times GMT

1000 NEWS SUMMARY

01 Jazz Now and Then

A cross-section of Jazz styles featuring new releases along with the classics. Presented by George Read.

15 Letter from America

Alistair Cooke's view of the USA.

30 Waveguide

The world of international radio broadcasting, with the latest developments in audio technology.

40 Bookchoice

A review of a newly published book.

45 From the Weeklies

A review of the week's top stories and features in the press.

1100 NEWSDESK

30 Meridian

A weekly programme about the arts.

1200 WORLD NEWS

15 Multitrack 3

Reggae, rock, rap or dance. Sarah Ward presents the best new releases from the alternative pop music scene, with interviews, features and competitions.

45 Sports Roundup

1300 NEWSHOUR

1400 NEWS SUMMARY

01 John Peel

A selection of pop from some of the more unusual and innovative music makers.

30 Sportsworld

The latest sporting events including: Winter Olympics from Lillehammer. Norway last hosted the Winter Olympics in 1952, when they finished top of the medals table. Competition will be fiercer this time though. In 1952 there were only 752 athletes, this time there will be over 2,000.

The Winter Olympics

The BBC broadcasts in 39 languages:

Albanian
Arabic
Bengali
Burmese
Bulgarian
Cantonese
Croatian
Czech
English
Finnish
French
German
Greek
Hausa
Hindi
Hungarian
Indonesian
Japanese
Mandarin
Nepali
Pashto
Persian
Polish
Portuguese
Romanian
Russian
Serbian
Sinhala
Slovak
Slovene
Somali
Spanish
Swahili
Tamil
Thai
Turkish
Ukranian
Urdu
Vietnamese

8 ▷ LOST PROPERTY

Before you watch

Have you ever lost anything very important?
What did you lose? When did you lose it?
Did you report it to the police?
Did you find it again?

While you watch

▶ **Watch the whole video and tick the things that Paola has lost.**

SECTION ONE

(*to* **David:** And a shoulder strap.)

Try to complete the lost property form.

LOST PROPERTY
Padstow Police Station

Date:

January 26th

Name of owner:

Object lost:

Where lost:

When lost:

Description:

▶ *Watch and check.*

SECTION TWO

(*to* **Paola:** Visa.)

What was in Paola's bag? There are some mistakes in the police officer's notes? Correct them.

Contents:

1/ *a black leather wallet*
(with 'Paola' in silver letters on it)

2/ *money: £40–50*

3/ *traveller's cheques: £200*

4/ *credit card: Access*

▶ *Watch and check.*

SECTION THREE

(*to the end*)

The police officer gives Paola some advice. What do you think it was? Complete these sentences.

THE POLICE
OFFICER'S ADVICE

1 If you lose your credit card, _____
_____

2 If you lose your traveller's cheques, _____
_____

3 If you lose your passport, _____
_____

4 If your bag turns up before Tuesday, we'll _____
_____

5 If you don't hear from us before Tuesday, _____
_____

▶ *Watch and check your ideas.*

Review

Are these sentences true or false? Correct the false ones.

	TRUE	FALSE
1 Paola left her bag on a bench near the beach at Harlyn bay.	☐	☐
2 P.C. stands for Police Cornwall.	☐	☐
3 Paola lost £200 in traveller's cheques.	☐	☐
4 The Italian consulate will give Paola a temporary passport.	☐	☐
5 Paola has the number of the Italian Consulate.	☐	☐
6 Paola thinks Cornwall is cold and boring.	☐	☐
7 The police officer gives Paola a lost property number.	☐	☐

After you watch

Summary

REPORTING A LOSS

I've lost my bag.
Is it likely to turn up?

POLICE

Can I help you?
Can you give me your name?
Can you give me the details?
When/Where did you lose it?
What kind of bag is it?
Can you describe it?
What was in the bag?
We'll give you a ring if it turns up.

DESCRIBING THINGS

It's black.
It's made of leather.
It has a gold buckle.

ACTIVITY ONE
Role-play: REPORTING LOST PROPERTY

Student A:
You are in Britain. You have lost something. Decide what you have lost and where and when you lost it. Go to the police station and report it.

Student B:
You are a police officer. Student A comes to the police station to report a loss. Ask questions and fill in the lost property form below.

POLICE Lost property	Description of object::
Date:	
Name and contact address of loser:	Contents (if any):
	Where lost?:
Object lost:	When lost?:

ACTIVITY TWO

Reading

Read the text and answer these questions.

1 What did 'highwaymen' do?
2 Who were 'constables'?
3 When did Robert Peel set up the Metropolitan Police?
4 How tall did the new policemen have to be?
5 What is the name of the headquarters of the Metropolitan Police?

The Origins of the British 'Bobby'

IN THE EIGHTEENTH century Britain's population doubled from six to twelve million. Many people moved into the towns and cities to work in the new factories. There was a lot of crime – especially violent crime and robbery, and people did not feel safe on the streets. On the roads outside the cities there were 'highwaymen' who stopped coaches and robbed the passengers.

At that time there were no professional policemen, only 'constables'. These were ordinary working people, like shopkeepers and farmers, who had to maintain order and catch criminals. But no one wanted to be a constable and most people paid money so that they would not have to be one!

However, by the 1820s crime in London was so bad that a government minister, Robert Peel, decided to start the Metropolitan Police. In 1829 he employed 3,000 policemen to patrol the streets of the capital. They had to be under 35 years old, over 5 feet 7 inches (170 cm) tall, healthy, and able to read. They wore a uniform – a blue coat, blue trousers (white in summer), and a black top hat – and carried a truncheon.

Their first office was in a small road called Scotland Yard – and this is still the name of the headquarters of the Metropolitan Police.

The people of London did not like the new policemen at first, and they called them 'Peelers' or 'Bobbies' after Robert Peel (Bobby is a short name for Robert). They laughed at them, and often disobeyed them.
But the police soon gained a reputation for being fair and brave, and for having a good sense of humour. People also began to feel safer on the streets of London.

Soon police forces were established in all the cities and counties of Britain.

9 ▷ THE MINI

Before you watch

Do you drive?
What kind of car do you drive?
What kind of car would you like to drive?

Look at the pictures of cars.

Which one is the Mini?
What do you know about
the Mini?
When was the Mini first made?
What are the other cars?
How would you describe them?

While you watch

1 Work in pairs. The following things and people all appear in the video. What connection do you think they have with the Mini?

5 million
1959
The British Motor Corporation
Alec Issigonis
two years
three metres
Enzo Ferrari
low centre of gravity
the Monte Carlo Rally

2 ▶ Watch the whole video and discuss the list again.

SECTION ONE

(*to* **Amanda**: ... big enough to carry four passengers.)

WHY ARE MINIS POPULAR?

1 Who says these things? Write B for Brian and K for Katie.

Katie Higginbottom

Brian Jones

a) ☐ They are a car that anybody can drive.
b) ☐ They're so economical.
c) ☐ They're very easy to drive around town.
d) ☐ I can maintain and service and repair them with small hand tools.
e) ☐ They're so well designed.
f) ☐ All of the controls are simple.
g) ☐ They're easy to park.
h) ☐ They last a long time.

▶ Watch and check.

2 What sort of car did BMC want to build? Choose five items from the box.

different	fast	small	expensive
cheap	elegant	economical	reliable
room for four passengers		comfortable	

▶ Watch and check.

SECTION TWO

(*to* **Amanda:** ... but which had more space inside.)

1 *Fill in the gaps on the picture, then* ▶ *watch and check.*

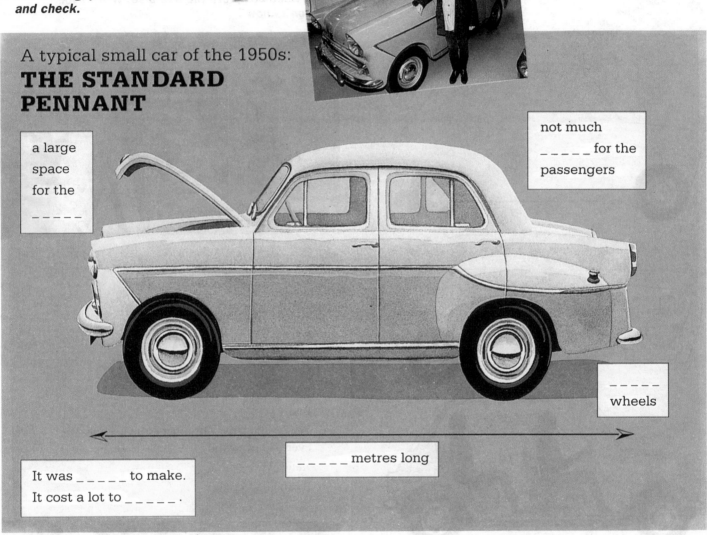

A typical small car of the 1950s:

THE STANDARD PENNANT

a large
space
for the
_ _ _ _ _

not much
_ _ _ _ _ for the
passengers

_ _ _ _ _
wheels

_ _ _ _ _ metres long

It was _ _ _ _ _ to make.
It cost a lot to _ _ _ _ _ .

2 *Are these sentences true or false?*

	TRUE	FALSE
a) The Mini was Alec Issigonis' first car.	☐	☐
b) Issigonis drew designs for the Mini on small pieces of paper.	☐	☐
c) From the first idea to the first complete car took two months.	☐	☐
d) Issigonis had to design a car that was bigger than most family cars.	☐	☐

▶ *Watch and correct the false ones.*

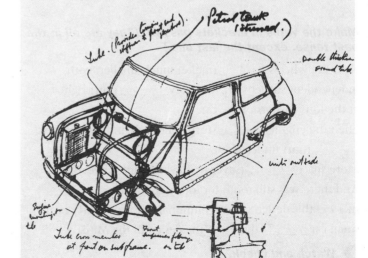

SECTION THREE

(*to* **Amanda:** … on the design of the Mini.)

THE PROBLEM IS SOLVED

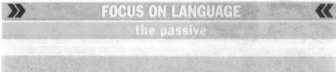

Make the verbs in brackets passive. (They are all in the past tense, except the last one.)

Next the wheels _ _ _ _ _ (make) much smaller, with independent suspension, and they _ _ _ _ _ (put) right at the four corners of the car.

Then the engine _ _ _ _ _ (turn) sideways and the gearbox _ _ _ _ _ (put) underneath.

More space _ _ _ _ _ (save) by having front-wheel drive. And there was still room for four passengers!

In 1959 this design was revolutionary. Today nearly every small car _ _ _ _ _ (base) on the design of the Mini.

▶ *Watch and check.*

SECTION FOUR

(*to* **Brian:** … with the boot lid laying down.)

1 What do Katie and Brian say? ▶ **As you watch the video complete the exercise. Write ? for 'I don't know'.**

a) How many Minis have you got *?*

    Katie _ _ _ _ _

    Brian _ _ _ _ _

b) Do you repair them yourself?

    Katie ☐ Yes ☐ No

    Brian ☐ Yes ☐ No

c) What's the fastest you've ever driven in a Mini?

    Katie _ _ _ _ _

    Brian _ _ _ _ _

d) What's the largest number of people you've ever had in a Mini?

    Katie _ _ _ _ _

    Brian _ _ _ _ _

SECTION FIVE

(*to* **Amanda**: ... in 1964, 1965, and 1967.)

RACING MINIS

1 Fill in the gaps in the text using words and phrases from the box.

> high-performance
> design
> family
> the rich
> low
> corners

By the mid-1960s the Mini was both a popular _ _ _ _ _ car
and a fashion accessory for _ _ _ _ _ . But something even
more surprising was happening: the Mini was becoming a
very successful _ _ _ _ _ car.

The unique _ _ _ _ _ – especially the position of the wheels
with their independent suspension, and the car's _ _ _ _ _
centre of gravity – meant that Minis were very fast,
especially when going round _ _ _ _ _ .

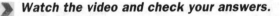 **Watch the video and check your answers.**

2 **Watch the video to the end and answer
the questions.**

  a) How many times did Minis win the Monte Carlo
    Rally? Why did they win?

  b) Are Katie and Brian happy with their Minis?

3 What do you think?

Do you think that the Mini is a good car? Why/Why not?
Would you like to own a Mini? Why?/Why not?

Review

***Read the three texts below. Which is the best summary
of the video?***

TEXT A

The Mini is Britain's most successful car. In the 1950s BMC
wanted to build a small economical 'people's car', but the
designer, Alec Issigonis, wanted to design a car that could
win the Monte Carlo Rally. Issigonis' design for the Mini
was revolutionary. He put the wheels right at the four
corners of the car, which meant that the Mini was very fast
when going round corners. His dream came true, and Minis
won the Monte Carlo Rally three times in the 1960s.

TEXT B

In the 1950s BMC wanted to build a small economical car
that would carry four passengers. The result was the Mini. It
was designed by Alec Issigonis. His design was revolutionary:
He turned the engine sideways and put the wheels right at
the four corners of the car. This left plenty of space for the
passengers. But two very surprising things happened. First,
the Mini became a very fashionable car, and many famous
people bought them. Second, the Mini became a successful
high-performance car and won the Monte Carlo Rally three
times in the 1960s.

TEXT C

The Mini is Britain's most successful car. Over 5 million have
been made. In the 1950s BMC wanted to build a small,
high-performance car that would be popular with film stars
and pop stars. So everybody was very surprised when the
Mini became a very popular family car, like the Volkswagen
Beetle in Germany. The Mini was designed by Alec Issigonis.
He turned the engine sideways and put the wheels right at
the four corners of the car. So, although the Mini was only
three metres long, there was plenty of room for four
passengers.

After you watch

ACTIVITY

Reading

You are going to read about Alec Issigonis, the man who designed the Mini.

MV 40F

1 Read the text. Here are the answers to some questions. What are the questions?

a) In Izmir, Turkey.

b) No, he was taught by a private teacher at home.

c) Engineering.

d) Three times.

e) In 1956.

f) Because the Suez Crisis caused petrol shortages in Europe.

g) Because he didn't listen to the radio himself.

2 What do you think?

a) Do you think Issigonis was right always to follow his instincts?

b) Do you think Issigonis was easy to work with?

ALEC ISSIGONIS

ALEC ISSIGONIS was born in 1906 in Izmir, Turkey. His mother was German and his father was Greek with British citizenship. Issigonis didn't go to school. He was taught by a private teacher at home.

After the First World War, the family moved to Britain, and Issigonis studied engineering. He was already a good designer but he couldn't do maths. He failed his maths exam three times at technical college!

He worked for a number of car manufacturers before joining Morris in 1936. After the Second World War he designed the Morris Minor, the first British car to sell over a million. In 1956 he joined the British Motor Corporation. In that year the Suez Crisis caused petrol shortages in Europe, so everyone wanted cars that did not use much petrol. Issigonis was asked to design a small economical car that could take four passengers. The result was the Mini.

Issigonis had complete control over the design of the Mini. He was an arrogant man who did not like to listen to other people. For example, he was told that all modern cars should have radios and seat belts. But he did not listen to the radio himself or wear seat belts, so he refused to put them in the first Minis. Later he changed his mind and seat belts and radios were added.

He saw himself as an artist rather than a scientist. He once said, 'Mathematics is the enemy of every truly creative man.' Issigonis always followed his instincts. Luckily, they were usually right!

10 ▷ INTRODUCTIONS

Before you watch

What do you do and say when you meet people for the first time in your country/in Britain?

What do you do and say when you go to someone's house for the first time in your country/in Britain?

While you watch

Who does these things? Write D for David, P for Paola, M for David's mother, and F for David's father.

☐ puts the kettle on

☐ goes to answer the door

☐ takes Paola's coat

☐ introduces Paola to Mr Evans

☐ gives Mrs Evans a box of chocolates

☐ and ☐ go and make the tea

☐ and ☐ stay in the sitting-room, talking

☐ tells Paola that her English is very good

☐ asks Paola how long she is there for

▶ **Watch the whole video and check your ideas.**

Paola

David

David's mother

David's father

SECTION ONE

(*to* **Mr Evans:** Please take a seat, Paola. **Paola:** Thanks.)

1 Put these six photos in the correct order. Number the first box in each photo.

2 Fill in the gaps in the six conversations.

3 Match the conversations with the photos.

A

Mrs Evans: David, _ _ _ _ _ Paola's coat, dear.

David: Yes, Mum.

B

Mrs Evans: It's _ _ _ _ _ to meet you. We've _ _ _ _ _ so much about you.

Paola: I'm very _ _ _ _ _ to meet you, Mrs Evans.

Mrs Evans: Please _ _ _ _ _ me Janet.

C

Paola: These are for you.

Mrs Evans: That's very _ _ _ _ _ of you. I love these.

D

David: Can I _ _ _ _ _ you to Paola?

Mr Evans: Hello, Paola. Pleased to meet you.

Paola: Hello, Mr Evans.

E

Mr Evans: Please, take a _ _ _ _ _, Paola.

Paola: Thanks.

F

Mrs Evans: _ _ _ _ _ in, _ _ _ _ _ in.

▶ **Watch and check.**

SECTION TWO

(*to* **Mrs Evans:** Don't forget the milk, dear.)

1 ▶ *Watch the video, then answer these questions:*

a) What does Mr Evans say that Paola should do?

_____

b) What does Mrs Evans think of Paola?

_____

c) What does Mrs Evans say about David and Paola's relationship?

_____

2 What do you think?

a) What do Mr and Mrs Evans think of David's relationship with Paola?

b) How do David and Paola feel about this?

☐ embarrassed ☐ surprised ☐ impatient
☐ angry ☐ irritated

c) Do young people in your country have similar problems communicating with their parents?

SECTION THREE

(*to the end*)

Who says these things? Write D for David, P for Paola, M for David's mother, and F for David's father.

☐ We might go there for our anniversary, mightn't we, Geoffrey?

☐ I can show you round.

☐ Doesn't David speak to you in Italian, then?

☐ I would speak Italian, but Paola's English is so good.

☐ Most of my friends don't speak much English.

☐ How long are you here for?

☐ Oh, what a shame!

▶ *Watch and check your ideas.*

Review

Are these sentences true or false? Correct the false ones.

	TRUE	FALSE
1 Mr Evans teaches art.	☐	☐
2 Paola would like a cup of tea.	☐	☐
3 Paola thinks Cornwall is very beautiful.	☐	☐
4 Mr and Mrs Evans were engaged for six months.	☐	☐
5 Mr and Mrs Evans went to Rome for their honeymoon.	☐	☐
6 David didn't speak Italian when he was in Rome at Easter.	☐	☐
7 Paola has to go back to Italy the day after tomorrow.	☐	☐

After you watch

Summary

MEETING PEOPLE

Pleased to meet you.
It's lovely to meet you.
I'm very pleased to meet you.
We've heard so much about you.
Please call me Janet.
Come in.
Please take a seat.

INTRODUCING PEOPLE

This is Paola.
Can I introduce you to Paola?

GIVING AND RECEIVING PRESENTS

This is/These are for you.
That's very kind of you.
I love this/these!

ACTIVITY ONE

Role-play: MEETING PEOPLE FOR THE FIRST TIME/
INTRODUCING PEOPLE

Work in groups of three or four.

Student A:
You are bringing a friend or partner to meet your parents for the first time. Introduce them.

Student B:
You are Student A's friend or partner. They are taking you to meet their parents for the first time. Give the parents a present.

Student C/D:
You are Student A's mother or father. Student A is going to introduce you to their friend or partner. Tell Student A to take their coat, then offer drinks and make polite conversation.

ACTIVITY TWO

Reading

1 Read the text, then answer the questions by ticking the correct boxes.

JAPANESE HOSPITALITY

When people visit each other in Japan, they usually take a present. This might be chocolates, or a box of cakes or biscuits (e.g. rice biscuits). They do not often take flowers as these are usually given to people in hospital.

When the guests arrive, they take their shoes off before stepping inside the house. The host will provide slippers for them to wear. Slippers are worn everywhere in the house except on 'tatami mats'. In most modern Japanese houses only one room has tatami on the floor and this is reserved for entertaining guests.

The meal is served on a low table and everyone sits on the floor. The host will sit facing the door. If the husband of the family has invited a business colleague to dinner, the wife will serve them but will not eat with them. She will join them at the end of the meal and ask the guest a few polite questions.

The meal will last quite a long time, perhaps two or three hours. Men drink beer or sake (rice wine) with their meal, sometimes quite a lot. (It is not impolite for men to get drunk in Japan.) Women only drink a little. It is impolite to fill your own glass in Japan – you should always look and see if anyone else's glass is empty and fill that first.

Traditionally the Japanese do not eat desserts, but they may serve cakes made of sweet red beans or western cakes. When the host serves green tea or coffee, it is a sign that the meal is nearly over, so that the guests know when to leave.

a) Which presents do guests usually bring?

☐ a box of rice biscuits ☐ some flowers
☐ a box of chocolates ☐ a bottle of wine

b) What do guests wear inside the house?

c) How is the meal served?

d) What do people drink with their meal?

☐ sake ☐ beer ☐ water
☐ whisky ☐ wine

2 Are these sentences true or false? Correct the false ones.

	TRUE	FALSE
a) If a man invites a colleague to dinner, his wife will not usually eat with them.	☐	☐
b) The meal lasts about an hour.	☐	☐
c) It is not impolite for men to get drunk.	☐	☐
d) It is not impolite to fill your own glass.	☐	☐

3 What happens in your country when people visit each other?

11 > THE VILLAGE

Before you watch

Do you live in the city or in the country?
What is the difference between city life and village life in your country?
What are the advantages of living in a small community?
What are the disadvantages?

1 Put these words into the columns.

crowds   farm   community spirit
horses   agriculture   good facilities
friendly   cinema   quiet   traffic jams
peaceful   commuter   village
communications   noise   good
pollution   industrial   motorway

CITY LIFE	COUNTRY LIFE

This video report is about King's Sutton, a small village in Northamptonshire.

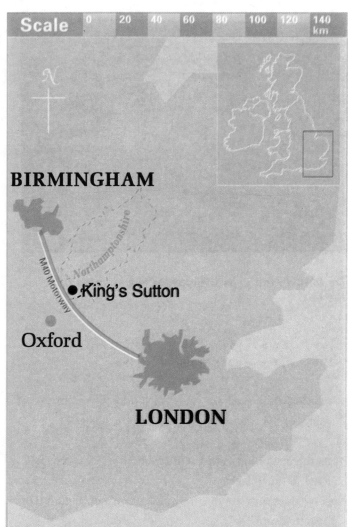

2 Fill in the gaps using words from the box.

bakery   complaints   affect
housing estate   self-sufficient   newcomers

a) The village used to be _ _ _ _ _ . People grew all their own food and lived without help from others.

b) People used to buy their bread from the _ _ _ _ _ .

c) They have built a new _ _ _ _ _ on the edge of the village.

d) The population of the village has doubled, but most of the _ _ _ _ _ do not work in the village.

e) The new motorway passes very close to the village. How does it _ _ _ _ _ life there?

f) They have received a lot of _ _ _ _ _ from the residents about noise from the motorway.

While you watch

Try to fill in the gaps with numbers and dates from the box.

7	2	40
1915	1,000	1992
1945	three or four hundred	

1 King's Sutton is about _ _ _ _ _ from Birmingham.

2 Many of the houses in the centre of the village are _ _ _ _ _ years old.

3 At the beginning of this century about _ _ _ _ _ people lived in the village.

4 Nowadays only about _ _ _ _ _ % of the population work in agriculture.

5 Elsie Merry's father came to the bakery in _ _ _ _ _ .

6 The bakery closed _ _ _ _ _ years ago.

7 The population of the village has doubled since _ _ _ _ _ .

8 A new motorway between London and Birmingham was completed in _ _ _ _ _ .

▶ **Watch the whole video and check your answers.**

SECTION ONE

(*to* **Michael:** ... at the local shops.)

FOCUS ON LANGUAGE
tense review

Fill in the gaps using verbs from the box. Put the verbs into the correct tense.

do	be	travel	need	happen
change	live	work (×2)	can	

But life here _ _ _ _ _ _ _ _ _ _ a lot and most of the changes _ _ _ _ _ _ _ _ _ _ during this century.

King's Sutton used _ _ _ _ _ _ _ _ _ _ a farming community. At the beginning of this century about a thousand people _ _ _ _ _ in the village and most of them _ _ _ _ _ on farms in the area. But nowadays machinery _ _ _ _ _ the work of horses and men, and only seven percent of the population _ _ _ _ _ in agriculture.

In the past the villagers rarely _ _ _ _ _ outside the village. They _ _ _ _ _ buy almost everything they _ _ _ _ _ at the local shops.

▶ **Watch and check your answers.**

SECTION TWO

(to **Michael:** ... not by bicycle, but by car and train.*)*

THE VILLAGE BAKERY

1 Are these sentences true or false?

	TRUE	FALSE
a) The baker still makes bread for the whole village.	☐	☐
b) Elsie Merry was born in the village.	☐	☐
c) Elsie's father came to the bakery in 1915.	☐	☐
d) The bakery opened in 1902.	☐	☐
e) They got up at 5 o'clock every morning and at 3 o'clock on Sunday.	☐	☐

▶ *Watch and correct the false ones.*

2 ▶ *Watch and answer these questions.*

a) Many of the shops in King's Sutton have closed. Why is this strange?

`_____`

b) Where do the newcomers live?

`_____`

c) Where do the villagers work and do their shopping?

`_____`

The General Stores in King's Sutton closed down in 1990

SECTION THREE

(to **Woman:** ... we wanted to be in a village.*)*

WHAT DO THE RESIDENTS THINK OF KING'S SUTTON?

1 *Who says these things?* ▶ *As you watch, write the numbers in the boxes.*

☐ The only thing I don't like is that everyone knows your business.

☐ It's friendly. It has good facilities, good communications.

☐ Quite a bit goes on, so it's quite interesting. And it's reasonably peaceful.

☐ I like it living here better than anywhere else, really.

2 *Can you remember anything else that they said?*

>> **FOCUS ON LANGUAGE** <<
second conditional

3 *Do these people think that life would be better if they lived in a town?* ▶ *As you watch, tick the correct boxes.*

a ☐ Yes ☐ No   b ☐ Yes ☐ No

c ☐ Yes ☐ No   d ☐ Yes ☐ No

4 *Can you remember any of the reasons they gave?* ▶ *Watch again.*

SECTION FOUR

(to the end)

THE MOTORWAY

Fill in the gaps in Peter Tombs' answers using
words from the box.

> noise   traffic jams   village   pollution
> commute   residents   comfortable   electricity

Peter: Well, there's a lot of complaint about the _ _ _ _ _
and _ _ _ _ from the motorway. But it does improve
communications for those who use cars for travel. And a
lot of them work in London, so they can _ _ _ _ _ quite
easily down there now, providing there are no _ _ _ _ _

Michael: So, is life in King's Sutton better than it was in
the past or worse?

Peter: It's better in the sense that we have gas, water,
_ _ _ _ _ and main drainage, so life for most people is
more _ _ _ _ _ _. The _ _ _ _ _ has doubled in size, but the
trouble is that most of the new _ _ _ _ _ don't work in the
village, so they are commuters. So we've lost a lot of the
community spirit which used to exist.

> **Watch and check.**

Review

**1 How has King's Sutton changed? Look at the sentences
in the first column and then write sentences about King's
Sutton as it is now in
the second column.**

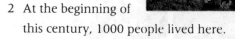

IN THE PAST ...	NOW ...
1 This was the whole village. ➤	1) _**Now the village is much bigger.**_ ____
2 At the beginning of this century, 1000 people lived here.	2) _____
3 King's Sutton used to be a farming community. Most of the people worked on farms in the area.	3) _____
4 Villagers rarely travelled outside the village. They could buy almost everything they needed at local shops.	4) _____
5 The baker used to bake bread for the whole village.	5) _____
6 There was no mains gas, water or electricity, so life was not very comfortable.	6) _____
7 There was a very strong community spirit.	7) _____

2 What do you think?

Does King's Sutton seem a nice place to live?
How has rural life changed in your country
in the last 100 years?
Is life better now than it was in the past?

After you watch

ACTIVITY

Look at the photos of the village as it was and as it is now. How has it changed?

Situation

12 ▷ FAREWELL

Before you watch

In your country how do you say goodbye to friends /
colleagues / members of your family?
What do you do? What do you say?

While you watch

SECTION ONE

(*to where David and Paola get into the car*)

1 David and Paola are about to leave David's parents' house. Before you watch, what do you think they will all say to each other when they leave?

2 What do you think they will do as they say goodbye, kiss or shake hands?

Paola and Mr Evans:

_____

Paola and Mrs Evans:

_____

David and Mrs Evans:

_____

David and Mr Evans:

_____

3 ▶ **Watch the video and check your ideas.**

4 Who says these things? Write P for Paola. D for David, M for David's mother, and F for David's father.

- [ ] Thank you for lunch.
- [ ] You're welcome, dear.
- [ ] I hope we see you again soon.
- [ ] And remember, you're welcome any time.
- [ ] If you come to Rome, you must let me know.
- [ ] Thanks for a lovely weekend.
- [ ] Safe journey.
- [ ] Take care of yourselves.

▶ **Watch again and check your answers.**

SECTION TWO

(*to* **David:** Are you sure we can't …*)

▶ **Watch the video, then answer these questions.**

1 How is David feeling?

_____

2 What do you think he is trying to say?

_____

SECTION THREE

(*to* **David**: Maybe you could come and live here.)

▶ *Watch the video, then discuss this question.*

Do you agree with Paola or David? Is it possible to have a relationship with someone who's living in another country?

SECTION FOUR

(*to* **David**: I doubt it.)

1 How will the conversation continue? Do you think that Paola will change her mind? ▶ **Watch the video. Were you right?**

2 Answer these questions.

a) How do you think David is feeling now?

_____

b) How do you think Paola is feeling?

_____

SECTION FIVE

(to the end)

1 What do you think Paola will do? ▶ **Watch the video. Were you right?**

2 Discuss this question.

What do you think will happen between David and Paola now?

Review

Is this information true or false? Correct the false sentences.

	TRUE	FALSE
1 Paola kisses Mr Evans when she says goodbye.	☐	☐
2 David shakes hands with his father when he says goodbye.	☐	☐
3 Paola is staying in Cornwall for two more days.	☐	☐
4 David and Paola discussed their relationship in Rome at Easter.	☐	☐
5 Paola thinks it would be impossible to have a relationship because they live in different countries.	☐	☐
6 Paola hopes that David will come and live in Italy.	☐	☐
7 Paola promises to keep writing to David.	☐	☐

▶ **Watch the whole video again and check your answers.**

After you watch

Summary

SAYING GOODBYE

HOSTS:
I hope we see you again soon.
Remember, you're welcome here any time.
Thank you for the chocolates.
Safe journey.
Drive carefully.
Take care of yourself/yourselves.

GUESTS:
Thank you for lunch.
Thanks for a lovely weekend.
If you come to Rome, you must let me know.
David has my address.

ACTIVITY ONE

Role-play: SAYING GOODBYE

Work in groups of two or three.

Student A:
You have just spent the day with Students B and C at their house. Thank them (for the meal, drinks, etc.) and tell them they can visit you any time.

Students B and C:
Student A has spent the day at your house. They are just leaving. Thank them for the present they gave you, and wish them a safe journey.

ACTIVITY TWO
Read David's letter to Paola.

22 East St
Bath
6 March

Dear Paola,

The copy of the article about Cornwall arrived this morning. Your photos look really great, especially the ones of the beach at Harlyn Bay.

I'm sorry to hear that you're having difficulty finding work in Rome. But keep looking — I'm sure something will turn up soon.

I wish you didn't have to stay in Italy. I wish you could come back to Britain. But you're right — you have your career to think about. And I can't really go and live in Italy — I'd never find a job. I suppose I could teach English . . .

Life here in Bath is much the same. Nothing very exciting to report. One piece of news — I'm going to join an evening class next week to improve my Italian. So I'll be able to buy you a proper cappuccino next time I come to Rome!

What are you doing at Easter? Have you made any plans yet? Would you like to meet up somewhere? How about Paris? Write and let me know what you think of the idea.

I saw mum and dad last weekend. They send their love. Mum still hopes to visit Rome for their wedding anniversary, if she can persuade dad to take her!

Anyway, I can't write any more. I've got to go to work. Boring!!!

Write soon, I'll phone. I miss you.

All my love,
David
XXX

Read these sentences. Write ✔ (true), ✗ (false) or ? (don't know) in the boxes.

1 Paola has written to David. ☐

2 Paola has found a job in Rome. ☐

3 David asks Paola to come back to Britain. ☐

4 Paola wants David to go and live in Italy. ☐

5 David has started an evening class in Italian. ☐

6 David suggests that they meet in Paris at Easter. ☐

7 David's parents are going to Rome for their anniversary. ☐

8 David stops writing because he is bored. ☐

ACTIVITY THREE
Imagine you are Paola, and write a reply to David's letter.

TRANSCRIPT

Situation

1 ▶ THE STATION

David: Good morning. Thanks. *(reading Paola's letter)*

Paola: Dear David, How are you? I'm sorry it's so long since I wrote to you, but I've been really busy looking for work. And at last I've got a job! A magazine called *In Viaggio* is sending me to Britain in January to take photos for an article on Cornwall. Can I visit you in Bath on my way there? I'm arriving on 22nd January. I can't stay very long but it would be nice to see you again. Please write soon and let me know if you'll be in Bath at that time. Sorry this is such a short letter – I'll give you my news when I see you. Love, Paola.

Station announcement: The next train to arrive at Platform 2 will be the 13.57 InterCity service to London Paddington calling at Chippenham, Swindon, Reading and London Paddington.

David: Excuse me. Can you tell me which platform the 1.45 from London comes in at?

BR employee: Platform 1. This platform.

David: Is it running on time?

BR employee: I think so. The arrivals information is on the screen up there.

David: Ah. Thanks.

Announcement: We would like to apologize to passengers waiting for the 13.55 service to Cardiff Central. This service is running approximately ten minutes late. The next train at Platform 1 will be the 13.45 InterCity service for Bristol Temple Meads only. This is the 12.20 service from London Paddington. The train now standing at Platform 1 is the 13.45 service for Bristol Temple Meads only.

David: It's great to see you. You're looking well.

Paola: So are you! Oh, roses! How lovely! Thank you.

David: Here, let me take your case. Phew! What have you got in here?

Paola: It's not that heavy, David!

David: How was the journey?

Paola: Not bad. I'm a bit tired, though!

David: What time did you leave Rome?

Paola: Oh, eight o'clock. But I got up at half past five.

David: Are you hungry?

Paola: No, I had a sandwich on the train.

David: When are you going to Cornwall?

Paola: Tomorrow.

David: My parents live down there. I was thinking of going to see them at the weekend. Perhaps we could meet up – I could even introduce you to them.

Paola: Yes that would be nice, but I've got a lot of work to do.

David: Oh, don't worry. I won't get in your way.

Paola: I didn't mean that. Just …

David: No, it's OK. Look, if you've got time, we can meet up. If not, well, never mind. I could drive you down to Cornwall, if you like.

Paola: I'm going to hire a car. The magazine is paying. But thanks anyway.

Report

2 ▶ SHERLOCK HOLMES

Amanda: All over the world, detective stories are the most popular kind of fiction. Everyone has their favourite detective, but who is the most famous detective of all?

Holmes: Well, we shall soon know.

Student A: Inspector Morse.

Holmes: I don't think so, Watson.

Student B: I think it's Sherlock Holmes.

Student C: Yes, Sherlock Holmes.

Student D: Well, Sherlock Holmes?

Student E: I think Sherlock Holmes.

Student F: Absolutely Sherlock Holmes.

Holmes: Is he?

Watson: Is he? You know he is.

Amanda: The Sherlock Holmes stories are famous everywhere, and it's the character of Holmes that makes them so popular. So, what sort of man was he?

Everybody knows what he looked like. He was tall and thin, with a long nose and sharp eyes. He smoked a pipe and carried a magnifying glass. And he wore a deerstalker hat. Although he is a fictional character, Sherlock Holmes had a real address – 221b Baker Street in London.

Today this is the Sherlock Holmes museum. Many people believe that Holmes was – or is – a real person. Every day letters for him arrive at this address!

Mrs Hudson: Oh, Dr Watson, this came by hand for Mr Holmes not ten minutes ago.

Watson: Thank you, Mrs Hudson.

Amanda: Holmes was a very intelligent man. He was an expert in chemistry and investigated crime like a scientist.

Holmes: The murderer came in through those French windows. There's the mud from the garden he brought in on his boots.

Amanda: That wasn't very difficult, was it?

Holmes: Elementary, my dear fellow.

Amanda: Sherlock Holmes had many other abilities, too. He was strong and athletic. He was a good boxer. And he was a master of disguise. He was also a superb violinist. In fact, he was the original Superman!

But there was another side to his character. Although he was very clever and successful, Holmes was a rather sad person. He thought everyday life was boring and depressing. When he was feeling miserable or bored, he spent all day in bed. And sometimes he took drugs.

Holmes: Drugs?

Amanda: Yes. He took cocaine – before it became illegal, of course.

He shared his flat with his only friend, Dr Watson. Holmes never fell in love, and he never married. He said that he didn't understand women. Dr Watson described him as 'a brain without a heart', 'more a machine than a man'.

Detectives are often more famous than the writers who create them. Let's see if people know who wrote the Sherlock Holmes stories.

Holmes: That's a very good idea.

Watson: Yes, a very good idea.

Student A: I don't know.

Student E: No, I don't know.

Student B: I don't know, sorry.

Student F: I don't know.

Amanda: The author of the Sherlock Holmes stories was Arthur Conan Doyle. He was born in Scotland, in 1859. He was a doctor, and he wrote detective stories in his spare time. Conan Doyle wrote twenty-six Sherlock Holmes stories between 1887 and 1895. Then, he decided to kill off his hero! Holmes' greatest enemy was Professor Moriarty.

Holmes: Oh, Professor Moriarty. And to what am I debted the pleasure of this visit.

Amanda: At the end of the story called *The Final Problem* Holmes and Moriarty fall into the Reichenbach Falls in Switzerland. But the Sherlock Holmes stories were very, very popular. Readers were very upset! Conan Doyle didn't like the Sherlock Holmes stories very much. He didn't think they were serious, and he wanted to write historical novels. But public pressure was too great, and he had to bring Holmes back to life. Conan Doyle continued writing stories about his detective hero for another twenty-five years.

I wonder if Sherlock Holmes will still be famous a hundred years from now? And will people still write to him?

Holmes: That's possible, quite possible.

Situation

3 ▶ CAR HIRE

David: Are you sure you don't want me to drive you down to Cornwall?

Paola: It's very kind of you, but ...

David: I can easily get the time off work.

Paola: David, I told you, the magazine is paying for the car. It really isn't necessary.

David: OK.

Paola: Look. You're coming to Cornwall at the weekend. We'll meet up then, OK?

David: Alright. I'm just going to get some petrol. I'll be back in about five minutes. Can you manage on your own?

Paola: Yes, no problem.

Clerk: Can I help you?

Paola: Yes, I'd like to hire a car for ... four days.

Clerk: What size of car would you like?

Paola: Small, please.

Clerk: Would you like an automatic or a manual?

Paola: Not automatic.

Clerk: Manual. Right. Just you, is it?

Paola: Yes.

Clerk: Well, I'd recommend a Ford Escort. For four days that would be £150. That includes VAT, unlimited mileage, and comprehensive insurance. But there's an excess of £75 on the insurance.

Paola: I'm sorry, what do you mean?

Clerk: Well, if it gets damaged, in an accident or a break-in, you have to pay the first £75, and the insurance company pays the rest.

Paola: OK. I understand.

Clerk: How would you like to pay?

Paola: By credit card. Visa.

Clerk: Thank you.

Paola: I'd like to leave the car at Heathrow Airport, if that's possible.

Clerk: That's no problem. But there's an additional charge of £50.

Paola: OK.

Clerk: Could I see your driving licence, please? Thank you. Could you give me a local contact address?

Paola: Yes. I'm staying at The Old Custom House Hotel, Padstow, in Cornwall.

Clerk: Do you know the telephone number?

Paola: No, I'm afraid I don't.

Clerk: That's OK. Right, the amount here is left blank until you return. The petrol tank is full when you start. If you return it full, no extra charge is made. OK, if you could just sign here. If you get any parking tickets or speeding fines, you have to pay them yourself. You mustn't take the vehicle outside the UK. If you could just sign here ... and here? Thank you. This is your part of the hire agreement. The car's outside. Someone will show you the controls.

Paola: Thank you.

Clerk: Thank you very much. Have a safe journey.

David: Bye.

Clerk: Bye.

David: We drive on the left, don't forget.

Paola: Very funny, David!

David: I'll see you on Saturday. Call me when you get to the hotel.

Paola: OK. And thanks for dinner last night, it was lovely.

David: Any time.

Paola: Goodbye.

David: Bye. Safe journey.

Report

4 ▶ PURPLE VIOLIN

Michael: Ed Alleyne-Johnson is a composer and violinist, but he doesn't play an ordinary violin. His music sounds like three or four instruments playing at the same time. But this deep, rich sound is produced by just one instrument: a purple electric violin.

Ed: I learnt to play the violin at school. I played in the school orchestra, but I didn't really enjoy playing classical music. It was too rigid. You have to play exactly what the composer wrote, and I wanted to experiment and improvise, and write my own music.

Michael: So, did you go to music college?

Ed: No, I studied painting at the School of Drawing and Fine Art in Oxford. But I carried on playing the violin in rock bands and folk bands.

Michael: So, what did you do when you left college?

Ed: I tried to make a career as a painter, but it was too difficult so I went back to music.

Michael: And that's when you started busking?

Ed: That's right. I started playing on the streets in England, and then I travelled round Europe and the States. I met a lot of different musicians in different countries and learnt some of the styles of music that they played.

Michael: Could you play us some?

Ed: Sure, yes. This is a typical Breton melody. And this is more of a Spanish sound.

Michael: That's great. So, did this European music influence your music?

Ed: It influenced me a lot. But my own music is a mixture of styles. I don't imitate them.

Michael: And have you stopped busking now?

Ed: No. I don't busk as much as I did, but I still enjoy it.

Not many people play electric violin on the street, so people are usually interested. When I write a new tune, I take it out on the street and play it to people. If they stop and listen, I think it must be good, so I develop it into a new piece. If they don't listen, it's back to the drawing-board.

Michael: Now, violins normally have four strings, don't they, Ed?

Ed: That's right.

Michael: Now, this has got five.

Ed: Yes, the top four strings are the same as an ordinary violin. The bottom string is the same as the C string on a viola. So, this is really a violin and a viola built into one.

Michael: Where did you get it?

Ed: I built this one myself.

Michael: Really? Did it take long?

Ed: It took longer to design than to build. About six months altogether.

Michael: Why did you paint it purple?

Ed: Oh, well, this is my first violin. I inherited it from my grandfather. When I got it, it was broken. So I repaired it and painted it purple to make it look nicer. Then, when I took it on the street busking, people noticed it and began to talk about it. "There's that guy with the purple violin." So when I built the new one, I decided to keep the colour. It's a sort of trade mark.

Michael: When you're playing it, it sounds like more than one instrument? How do you get such a rich sound out of it?

Ed: I use these effects pedals. They change the sound of the violin and make it sound like different instruments. For example, this one makes it sound a bit like an electric guitar. This one makes it sound like a cello or a bass. You can even make it sound like a steel band. Then I combine all the different sounds using an echo box.

Michael: What's an echo box?

Ed: Well, it's a device that records the music I have just played, and repeats it again and again. So, I can play a base line. The echo box carries it on while I play another part on top. Then it carries on repeating both those parts while I play the tune.

Michael: So, that's all the equipment you need if you are going to play live?

Ed: Yes, that's right. I can use this same equipment on the street or in a big concert. It's a sort of high-tech, one-man band.

Michael: Ed, so you've also made a CD, haven't you?

Ed: That's right. It's called 'The Purple Electric Violin Concerto' for obvious reasons. It was very cheap to make. Because of the way I work, I can record straight onto digital tape instead of having to use a big recording studio. Digital tape's a sort of high quality cassette that enables you to make a CD.

Michael: So, you did it all yourself?

Ed: That's right. Because there isn't a big record company behind it, I was free to record whatever I wanted.

Michael: So, how many copies have you sold?

Ed: About thirty thousand so far.

Michael: That's great. What about the future? What are your plans?

Ed: Well, the first CD is still selling well. At the moment I'm recording a new CD. And I'm going to go back to Europe and give free concerts on the streets and in record stores.

Michael: So you are going to carry on busking?

Ed: That's right. This music was inspired by the streets, and I'd like to take it back to the people who helped me to write it.

Situation

5 ▸ THE HOTEL

Receptionist: Here's your key. We've put you in room 10, that's on the first floor. It has a lovely view of the harbour. Shall I get somebody to help you with your bags?

Paola: No, thank you. I can manage.

Receptionist: OK.

Receptionist: Reception.

Paola: Yes, hello. This is Paola Calvetti in room 10. I'm afraid there aren't any towels in the bathroom.

Receptionist: Oh, I'm terribly sorry. I'll bring some up right away.

Paola: Thank you.

Paola: Come in.

Receptionist: Here are your towels. I do apologize. The chambermaid forgot to leave them.

Paola: It doesn't matter, really. Don't worry.

Receptionist: There you are. Is everything else OK?

Paola: Yes, it's fine.

Receptionist: Well, I hope you enjoy your stay.

Paola: Thank you.

Switchboard: Good afternoon. Bath Herald.

Paola: Could I speak to David Evans, please?

Switchboard: Just a moment, please.

David: Hello. David Evans here.

Paola: Hi, it's me.

David: Hi. You've arrived then.

Paola: Yes, I checked in a few minutes ago.

David: What's the hotel like?

Paola: It's on the sea front. It's quite small, but it's very clean and comfortable. I have a wonderful view of the harbour from my window. It's a beautiful village, David. It's very peaceful and quiet too.

David: How was the journey?

Paola: Oh, not too bad. I got stuck in a traffic jam near Exeter, but I wasn't held up for long.

David: Which side of the road did you drive on?

Paola: David!

David: Sorry.

Paola: When are you coming down?

David: On Friday night. Can we meet up on Saturday?

Paola: Yes, let's do that.

David: How do I get to the hotel?

Paola: It's very easy to find. It's on the harbour.

David: OK. I'll see you on Saturday, then. Be good.

Paola: Yes, OK. Bye.

David: Bye.

Voice: Room service.

Paola: Yes … could I have a coffee and a tuna sandwich, to room 10, please?

Voice: Certainly, madam. It'll be about ten minutes.

Paola: Thank you.

Report

6 ▸ WALES

Amanda: Wales is a country of lakes and mountains. It's about half the size of Switzerland, and it has a population of two and three quarter million.

Here in the north is some of the most beautiful scenery in the British Isles. Behind me is Snowdon, Britain's second highest mountain.

Wales is not an independent nation. In 1292, the English king, Edward 1, invaded Wales and built fourteen huge castles to control the Welsh people. His son, Edward, became the first Prince of Wales. Since then all the kings and queens of England have given their eldest sons the title, Prince of Wales. I'm sure you know who the latest one is.

Here, at Caernarfon Castle, Prince Charles became the twenty-first Prince of Wales. Although the English have ruled Wales for many centuries, Wales still has its own flag, its own culture and, above all, it's own language.

In the towns and villages of North Wales, many people speak English only as a second language. Their first language is Welsh.

This is Llanberis, a small town at the foot of Snowdon. Eighty-six per cent of the people here speak Welsh as their first language.

Elizabeth Roberts is the headmistress of Llanberis Primary School. In her school the children have nearly all their lessons in Welsh.

Ms Roberts: The language policy in the school is that children should be bilingual by the time that they are eleven years old. The children are taught in the medium of Welsh most of the time, but we do teach English to them as well.

Amanda: Is it a problem for them learning two languages instead of one?

Ms Roberts: No, not at all. What happens when a child learns two languages at the same time is that they have an insight into two cultures. They learn to read, so they have all the folk tales of two languages. And another thing that helps them is that they can pick up the third and fourth language without any problems at all.

Amanda: Which do you prefer English or Welsh?

Dawn: Welsh.
Claudia: Welsh.
Rhuys: I prefer Welsh.
Rebecca: Welsh.
Jack: In Welsh you spell things just how you say them, in English there are more silent letters.
Amanda: Can you tell me some English words in Welsh?
Rebecca: Chair is 'cadair'.
Dawn: Rainbow is 'enfys'.
Jack: Table is 'bwrdd'.
Joanna: Yes is 'Ie'.
Dafydd: Goodnight is 'nos da'.
Claudia: School is 'ysgol'.
Rhuys: How are you? is 'Sut ydych chi'.
Amanda: Welsh is one of the oldest languages in Europe. It is a Celtic language, like Breton in France, Gaelic in Ireland, or Gaelic in Scotland.

Two and a half thousand years ago Celtic languages were spoken in many parts of Europe. Most of these languages died out a long time ago when the Romans invaded these areas, but some Celtic languages have survived in the north-west corner of Europe.

So, the Welsh language has survived for more than two thousand years, but over the last hundred years the number of Welsh-speakers has fallen very quickly. Now only twenty percent of Welsh people speak Welsh.

English is now the first language in most of Wales, and it is possible that the Welsh language will die out. Many people now believe that it should be preserved. So, what are they doing about this? Well, all official forms and documents have to be in Welsh and English. And all road signs have to be bilingual, too. And since 1982 there has been a Welsh-language television channel. Most importantly of all, all children at school now have to learn Welsh. But is this enough? Will the language survive?

Ms Roberts: A lot has been done up to now to help the Welsh language: road signs, bilingual documentation, and there's a Welsh language act. But, I think, a lot more English

people have to be educated, and need to be told that we are a nation that stands by itself and have a language and our own culture.

Amanda: The future of Welsh is uncertain. The problem is that Welsh has to survive next door to English, and, as we all know, English is a very successful language.

Report

7 ▸ BBC WORLD SERVICE

Announcer: This is London ... Fifteen hours, Greenwich Mean Time.
Newsreader: BBC World Service ... the news. Read by ...

Michael: This is Bush House in London, headquarters of the BBC World Service. From this building the BBC broadcasts radio programmes to the whole world.

The World Service used to be called 'The Empire Service'. When it started in 1932, it broadcast only in English and provided news and information to people in the British colonies. This is a recording of the very first broadcast.

Recording: This is London calling. Before beginning our first programme, Mr J H Whitley, the chairman, and Sir John Reith, the director-general of the BBC, are going to speak to you.

Michael: The announcers used formal English and used to speak very slowly and clearly. After six o'clock they used to change into dinner-jackets to read the news.

In the 1930s Hitler and Mussolini started broadcasting propaganda to the Middle East.

So in 1938 the World Service also started broadcasting to the Middle East, in Arabic, to counteract the influence of the fascist propaganda. Very soon the BBC was broadcasting to all the countries occupied by the Nazis.

During the Second World War the BBC reported British defeats as well as British victories, and so it got a reputation for honesty and accuracy. After the war the BBC continued its foreign language broadcasts, and to this day broadcasts the news in · thirty-nine languages.

This is a live news broadcast to Somalia. Over forty percent of the population listen to these broadcasts every day because they cannot get accurate news and information in their own country.

Here in the Newsroom a hundred and twenty journalists work day and night, writing two hundred news bulletins every twenty-four hours.

Every news story is checked at least twice before it is broadcast. The BBC will not broadcast a story until it is sure that it is true.

When President Gorbachev was put under house arrest in the Soviet Union in 1991, he said that he learnt the truth about what was happening in his country by listening to the BBC World Service.

This means the World Service is not always popular with governments. For example, the former Soviet Union jammed the broadcasts for many years so that it was difficult for Russian people to listen to the BBC news. Even the British Government was very angry when the World Service broadcast a speech criticising the Government during the Suez Crisis in 1956.

The BBC is the world's largest international broadcaster. Every week, one hundred and thirty million people listen to BBC World Service radio. In 1992 the World Service started broadcasting television programmes, too, via satellite, to Europe, Asia and Africa. Now people in countries all around the world can see as well as hear the news from the BBC.

Situation

8 ▶ LOST PROPERTY

Paola: Where's my bag?
David: When did you last see it?
Paola: It's got everything in it – my passport, my money, my ID card, my credit cards …

David: You had it on the beach …
Paola: It must be on the bench.

Oh, no. It's not here. What am I going to do?
David: We'll have to report it to the police.

Police officer: Hello. Can I help you?
Paola: Yes, I've lost my bag.
Police officer: Right. Can you give me your name?
Paola: Paola Calvetti.
Police officer: Paola … C-A-L … ?
Paola: V-E-double T-I.
Police officer: You're Italian, are you?
Paola: Yes, I'm from Rome.
Police officer: Ah. Can you give me the details? Where did you lose it?
Paola: I left it on the bench …
David: Near the beach at Harlyn Bay.
Police officer: And you've been back to the bench?
David: Yes. We went back straight away, but it wasn't there.
Police officer: I see. When was this?
Paola: This morning. Just now.
Police officer: What kind of bag is it? Can you describe it?
Paola: It's black, made of leather, it has a gold …
David: Buckle.
Paola: Yes, a gold buckle.
David: And a shoulder strap.

Police officer: And what was in the bag?
Paola: Oh, my money, my traveller's cheques, my credit card.
Police officer: Were your money and card in a wallet or purse?
Paola: Yes, in a brown leather wallet.
David: The wallet has her initials – P.C. – in silver letters on it.
Police officer: Same as me.
Paola: Sorry?
Police officer: PC stands for 'Police Constable'. I'm PC Wilson. How much money was in the wallet?
Paola: About thirty or forty pounds, and £200 in traveller's cheques.
Police officer: And what credit card did you have?
Paola: Visa.
Police officer: Well, you should contact Visa and put a stop on the credit card. Contact the bank that issued the traveller's cheques, too, and let them know what's happened. What else was in the bag?
Paola: My passport. I have to go back to Italy in a few days. What happens if I can't find it?

Police officer: Don't worry. You must telephone the Italian Consulate in London immediately. They'll give you a temporary passport.
Paola: I don't have their number.
David: We can get it from Directory Enquiries.
Police officer: Can you give me an address in England where we can contact you?
Paola: The Old Custom House Hotel. I'm there until Tuesday, and then I go back to Italy.
Police officer: Are you on holiday here?
Paola: No. I'm a photographer. I'm taking photographs of Cornwall.
Police officer: Really? What, at this time of year?
Paola: It's beautiful in the winter – it's wild and romantic.
Police officer: I prefer it in the summer myself. Well, if your bag turns up before Tuesday, we'll give you a ring at your hotel.
Now, this is your lost property number, and here's the phone number of this police station. If you don't hear from us, give us a ring before you leave the country.
David: Is it likely to turn up?
Police officer: I don't know. It depends who found it.
Paola: OK. Thank you.
Police officer: Goodbye. I hope you enjoy the rest of your stay.
Paola: Thank you.
David: Goodbye.

Police officer: Yes, sir? Can I help you?
Young man: I found this bag on a bench at Harlyn Bay.

Report

9 ▶ THE MINI

Amanda: This is Britain's most popular and successful car, the Mini. Over five million have been made. This is one of the latest models.

And this is one of the very first Minis. It was made in 1959. As you can see, the design has hardly changed. Very few cars have lasted as long as the Mini. So why is it so popular?

Katie Higginbottom: I think because they are so well designed and so economical … and they last a long time. I can't think of any other cars that you see so many of them when they are so old. They are very easy to drive around town and easy to park, and just good cars to drive, really.

Brian Jones: The mini's so special for me because I can maintain and service and repair them with small hand tools within my own workshop. They are a car that anybody can drive. Most people have driven one at some time and all of the controls are simple and so, therefore, you don't have to relearn the car every time you get in it to drive.

Amanda: In the late 1950s, BMC, the British Motor Corporation, wanted to build a car that was different from other cars. They wanted it to be small, cheap, and economical – like the 'bubble car'. But the 'bubble car' could only take two passengers. BMC wanted a family car, big enough to carry four passengers.

Nowadays that doesn't sound like a difficult problem. But in 1957 it was. At that time a typical small family car looked like this. It was quite long about three and a half metres. It had large wheels, and large space for the engine. So there wasn't much room for the passengers. And it was expensive to make, and cost a lot to run.

The Mini was designed by Alec Issigonis. This wasn't his first car. In 1948 he designed the Morris Minor, which was also very successful. He was a fast worker. He drew designs for the Mini on small pieces of paper, even on the back of envelopes! From the first idea to the first complete car took just two years – an incredible achievement.

Issigonis' problem was this: how to design a car which was smaller than most family cars but which had more space inside.

First of all he decided that the Mini should be three metres long, half a metre shorter than most small cars. Next, the wheels were made much smaller, with independent suspension. And they were put right at the four corners of the car. Then, the engine was turned sideways, and the gearbox was put

underneath. More space was saved by having front-wheel drive. And there was still room for four passengers!

In 1959 this design was revolutionary. Today nearly every small car is based on the design of the Mini.

Like the Volkswagen Beetle in Germany, the Mini was designed as a peoples' car. It was cheap and economical and in the early 1960s many ordinary families in Britain bought one. Everybody was very surprised, then, when the Mini became a very fashionable car. Many famous people drove them: film stars, pop stars, politicians, royalty. Even Enzo Ferrari, the famous Italian sports car designer, owned one.

How many Minis have you got?
Katie: I've got two Minis, but only one of them goes.
Brian: I think at the last count fourteen.
Amanda: Do you repair them yourself?
Katie: Well, I have tried. But no, I get someone to do it for me, usually.
Amanda: What's the fastest you've ever driven in a Mini?
Brian: The fastest I've been in this particular one has been is about a hundred and twenty-five miles an hour.
Amanda: What's the largest number of people you've ever got in a Mini?
Katie: Oh, not very many. Only about five or six.
Brian: There were four of us actually in the front seat. And I think there were five in the back seat, and one was sitting in the boot with the boot lid laying down.

Amanda: By the mid-1960s the Mini was both a popular family car and a fashion accessory for the rich. But something even more surprising was happening: the Mini was becoming a very successful high-performance car.
The unique design – especially the position of the wheels with their independent suspension, and the car's low centre of gravity – meant that Minis were very fast, especially when going round corners.

Mini's took part in all the major

European rallies from 1960. There were a lot of bigger, faster cars in these races, such as the Porsche 911 and the Citroen DS, but on narrow, winding roads nothing could beat the Mini. These three Minis won the Monte Carlo Rally in 1964, 1965, and 1967.

Is there anything you don't like about the Mini?
Brian: I can honestly say no.
Katie: They're not very good when it's damp. When it rains, they're a bit tricky to start.
Amanda: Is there any other car you'd prefer to have?
Brian: Only something like a Porsche, but realistically, not really.
Amanda: Would you swap your Mini for another car?
Katie: Oh, no … I don't think so.

Amanda: The Mini is not the most elegant car. It's not the fastest car or the most comfortable, either. But it's got plenty of character; it's fun to drive; and although it's over thirty years old, it still looks good. And, of course, it's easy to park.

Situation

10 ▶ INTRODUCTIONS

Mrs Evans: They're here, Geoffrey. You go and put the kettle on. I'll answer the door.
Mr Evans: Yes, dear.

Paola: Now, tell me again about your parents. What does your father do?
David: I've told you before. He's a bank manager, and my mum teaches art.

Mrs Evans: Hello.
David: Hello, Mum. This is Paola.
Mrs Evans: It's lovely to meet you. We've heard so much about you.
Paola: I'm very pleased to meet you, Mrs Evans.
Mrs Evans: Please call me Janet. Come in, come in. David, take's Paola's coat, dear.
David: Yes, Mum.
Mrs Evans: Come into the sitting-room.
David: Dad, can I introduce you to Paola?
Mr Evans: Hello, Paola. Pleased to meet you.

Paola: Hello, Mr Evans. Oh, these are for you.

Mrs Evans: That's very kind of you. I love these. We can have some after lunch. Did you put the kettle on, Geoffrey?

Mr Evans: Yes, I did, dear.

Mrs Evans: Paola, would you like some tea, or would you prefer coffee?

Paola: Tea would be lovely.

Mrs Evans: Tea for you, David?

David: Yes, please, Mum. I'll come and help you.

Mr Evans: Please, take a seat, Paola.

Paola: Thanks.

Mr Evans: How are you enjoying your stay in England?

Paola: It's great. Cornwall is very beautiful.

Mr Evans: Yes, it's lovely, isn't it? But it's a bit wet at this time of year. David tells me you're a photographer.

Paola: Yes, that's right. I'm here taking photographs for a magazine.

Mr Evans: You should take photos for one of David's articles. You'd make a good team!

Mrs Evans: She's lovely, David.

David: Sshhh! She'll hear you.

Mrs Evans: It's must be very difficult for you, living in different countries.

David: We're not exactly going out together, Mum.

Mrs Evans: Well, you can't, can you, with her living in Rome and you in Bath.

David: I mean, she's not my ... girlfriend.

Mrs Evans: These things take time. Your father and I were engaged for six years before we got married. Don't forget the milk, dear.

Mr Evans: And you live in Rome, don't you, Paola?

Paola: Yes, that's right.

Mr Evans: Janet and I went there on our honeymoon ... but that was a long time ago.

Mrs Evans: Thirty years ago in May. We might go there again for our anniversary, mightn't we, Geoffrey?

Paola: If you do, you must come and see me. I can show you round.

Mrs Evans: That would be lovely.

Mr Evans: Your English is very good, Paola.

Paola: Thank you. I go to evening classes in Rome. And of course, I practise on David.

Mr Evans: Doesn't David speak to you in Italian, then?

Paola: Not very much.

Mrs Evans: Oh, David! And you studied it for years at school.

David: For two years. I would speak Italian, but Paola's English is so good. I spoke Italian when I was in Italy at Easter.

Paola: He did. He tried very hard – he had to, most of my friends don't speak much English.

Mrs Evans: How long are you here for, Paola?

Paola: I have to go back to Italy the day after tomorrow.

Mrs Evans: Oh, what a shame!

Report

11 ▸ THE VILLAGE

Michael: In the heart of the English countryside you feel that life hasn't changed for centuries. Here it is quiet and peaceful. People can escape from the cities and their crowds, pollution, and noise.

This is King's Sutton, a village in Northamptonshire, about forty miles from the huge industrial city of Birmingham.

Many of the houses in the centre of the village are three or four hundred years old. This square certainly hasn't changed much. For centuries, this was the whole village. At the end of the square stands the church of St Peter and St Paul. It was built between 1220 and 1450, and is the oldest building in the village.

But life here has changed a lot and most of the changes have happened during this century.

King's Sutton used to be a farming community. At the beginning of this century about a thousand people lived in the village and most of them worked on farms in the area.

But nowadays machinery does the work of horses and men, and only seven per cent of the population work in agriculture.

In the past, the villagers rarely travelled outside the village. They could buy almost everything they needed at the local shops. (Morning).

This was the village bakery. The baker used to make bread for the whole village. But I don't think any bread has been made here recently. Elsie Merry was born in the village and has lived here all her life. Her father was the village baker.

Elsie, When did your father open the bakery?

Elsie: He came to the bakery in 1915. It had always been the bakery from 1802. But he came in 1915 during the First World War.

Michael: Was it hard work baking bread?

Elsie: Very hard work. Yes, yes. Up at five o'clock in the morning, three o'clock on Saturday morning always.

Michael: So, when did the bakery close?

Elsie: Two years ago. Two years last Easter.

Michael: Many of the other shops have closed, too. That's strange, because there are now two thousand people living here – the population has doubled since 1945.

And the village is much bigger. New housing estates have been built for the newcomers. But not many of the people who live in these houses work in the village.

You see, King's Sutton isn't a self-sufficient community any more. The villagers work in nearby towns, and they do most of their shopping there too in large supermarkets. How do they get there? Not by bicycle. But by car and train.

Why do you like living in King's Sutton?

Jill Rhodes: It's friendly. It has good facilities, good communications. It's just a good community.

Margaret Tombs: I like the people mostly. Quite a bit goes on, so it's quite interesting. And it's reasonably peaceful.

Debbie: I like the village life. I've always lived here. I like the community life. The only thing I don't like is that everybody knows your business.

Sophie: I like it living here better than anywhere else, really.

Michael: If you lived in the town do you think life would be better?

Laura: Well, I don't think life would be better, because there'd be a lot more noise and danger and stuff like that.

Simon: Well, you could go to the cinema. You could go swimming. There'd be better sports facilities.

Debbie: I think there'd be more to do ... probably more people.

Sue: We came here because we didn't want to be in a town. We wanted to be in a village.

Michael: A new motorway between London and Birmingham was completed in 1992, and it passes close to the village. How does this affect village life?

Peter Tombs: Well, there's a lot of complaint about the noise and pollution from the motorway. But it does improve communications for those who use cars for travel. And a lot of them work in London, so they can commute quite easily down there now, providing there are no traffic jams.

Michael: So, is life in King's Sutton better than it was in the past, or worse?

Peter: It's better in the sense that we have gas, water, electricity and main drainage, so life for most people is more comfortable. The village has doubled in size, but the trouble is most of the new residents don't work in the village, so they're commuters. So we've lost a lot of the community spirit which used to exist.

Michael: It's still quite strong, though.

Peter: It's still quite strong, especially amongst the older people.

Michael: Life in King's Sutton has changed a lot during this century. If more and more people move out of the cities, the village will continue to change. But let's hope that here at the heart of King's Sutton there will always be peace and quiet.

Situation

12 ▶ FAREWELL

Paola: Thank you for lunch.

Mrs Evans: You're welcome, dear. And thank you for the chocolates.

Mr Evans: I hope we see you again soon, Paola.

Paola: Yes, I hope so.

Mrs Evans: And remember, you're welcome any time.

Paola: Thank you. If you come to Rome, you must let me know. David has my address.

Mrs Evans: Thank you, Paola.

Paola: So ... thank you. Goodbye.

Mr Evans: Goodbye.

Mrs Evans: Ooh, Italian style!

Mr Evans: Bye, David. See you next month in Bath.

David: Yes. Bye, Dad. Bye, Mum. Thanks for a lovely weekend.

Mrs Evans: Bye, dear.

Mr Evans: Safe journey.

Mrs Evans: Drive carefully, David. Take care of yourselves.

Paola: Your mum and dad are really nice, David.

David: They liked you, too. It's a pity I've got to go back to Bath tonight. I wish I could stay here a bit longer with you.

Paola: I'm only staying here for one more day myself.

David: Even one day would be nice.

Paola: I want to take some more photographs of the harbour. If it stops raining.

David: OK.

David: I've really missed you, Paola. Are you sure we can't ...

Paola: David, we talked about this in Rome at Easter, didn't we?

David: I know, Paola ...

Paola: I'm sorry, David. I just think it's best if we stay friends. I live in Italy, you're here. It would be impossible.

David: How do you know? We haven't tried it yet.

Paola: It just wouldn't work. When would we see each other?

David: Well, on holidays, at first. And then maybe you could come and live here?

Paola: I can't make that sort of commitment. I just can't make promises like that.

David: There's nothing I can say to make you change your mind ...

Paola: We've been friends for a long time, David. Let's not change it now, please.

David: OK. But make sure you keep writing.

Paola: I will. I promise. I'd love a coffee. Can we get a cappuccino anywhere round here?

David: I doubt it.

Paola: David!